The Lucifer Gospel

A **FINN RYAN** CONSPIRACY THRILLER

PAUL CHRISTOPHER

THE LUCIFER GOSPEL

CANELO

First published in the United States in 2006 by Onyx, an imprint of New American Library, a division of Penguin Group (USA) Inc

This edition published in the United Kingdom in 2019 by

Canelo Digital Publishing Limited
57 Shepherds Lane
Beaconsfield, Bucks HP9 2DU
United Kingdom

A CIP catalogue record for this book is available from the British Library.

Print ISBN 978 1 78863 401 4
Ebook ISBN 978 1 78863 225 6

Look for more great books at www.canelo.co

Printed and bound in Great Britain by Clays Ltd, Elcograf S.p.A.

For Lloyd and Sharon because they deserve one at last, my friends in the Czech Republic

1

The American Airlines 777 circled the ancient city, invisible within a dark brown smudge of air pollution. Finn Ryan stared out her window on the wide-body jet and frowned. For her first sight of the land of the pharaohs it wasn't a very inspiring view. Pittsburgh on the Nile.

"Urine," said the man in the seat beside her. He was craning his neck for a look out the window. He was in his early thirties, dark-haired and handsome if you liked the slightly beat-up, untidy look.

"Pardon me?" Finn answered. She was younger than he was, red-haired and beautiful.

"Urine," the man repeated. "That's the first thing you notice when you get off the plane. "The whole place smells like pee."

"Thanks for sharing," said Finn.

The man grinned, his whole face brightening. "Every city has its own particular smell, have you noticed that? London smells like a wet cigar, Dublin smells exactly like a brewery... which figures, I guess. Hong Kong reeks like the inside of a chicken farm, New York has this faint undertone of rotting garbage."

"I never noticed that about New York," said Finn. Most of her life had been spent in her home-town of

Columbus, and then New York City, where she now lived. She hadn't done an awful lot of traveling.

"That's because you live there, right?" said the man. "You've gotten used to it, that's all, but it's there, believe me. Prague smells exactly like a leftover pork roast. Geneva smells like room deodorizer, Paris smells like an old lady's shoes. In Saigon it's fish soup. It's true."

Finn tried to remember if Columbus had any particular odor. The only thing she could recall was the cool tang of the Scioto River in the summer and apple blossoms in the spring. "What does it smell like where you come from?" she asked.

"A giant car ashtray," he said. "Los Angeles." He held out his hand. "My name's Hilts."

She took the hand briefly. The grip was strong and dry. "Finn Ryan."

"Finn. Short for Fiona, right?"

"That's right," she said and nodded, surprised. He was quick.

"I like Finn better. Fiona's kind of... prudish, I guess."

She decided not to respond to that. "Do you have a first name?"

"Hilts. Just Hilts." He pointed his chin out the window. "First time in Cairo?"

Finn nodded. "First time anywhere, really. I just got my master's. It seems like I've spent my whole life in school."

"Vacation?"

"Job. Technical illustrator for an archaeological expedition." She liked the sound of that. Archaeological expedition. It brought up images of men in pith helmets and King Tut's tomb. Agatha Christie mysteries. She froze at the thought of the word "mystery." She'd had enough of that kind of thing the year before to last her a lifetime. She remembered the dying map in the old crypt tunnel and shivered.

"Sounds interesting."

"We'll see." Finn shrugged. "It's in Libya. The first time they've allowed an American dig there in more than fifty years."

"Libya hasn't been on the best terms with us for a while," Hilts said. "The western desert is kind of spooky. It really is like a frozen sea. The worst storm ever, sculpted out of sand. The dunes are like the biggest Hawaiian surfing waves you've ever seen, except bigger, and even more dangerous, except for different reasons." He paused, his grin replaced by a grimace. "The part that's not dunes is even worse, like an endless rocky beach with no ocean. Boiling in the daytime, freezing cold at night. It's where Dante got his idea for Hell."

"You've been there?"

Hilts laughed. "Sweetheart, I've been everywhere."

She looked at him; it wasn't a boast, just a statement of fact. The word "sweetheart" came out like a travel-weary sigh. "So what do you do that takes you everywhere?" Finn asked.

"I'm a photographer," he answered. Suddenly the aircraft leaned heavily to the right. Finn held her breath. The conversation was cut short by the pinging of the public-address system and the stewardess announcing their final approach. They were landing.

2

Finn was swept out of the aircraft along with five hundred other passengers, most of them Egyptians coming home on vacation to see their families. She moved through the laughing, chattering crowd, eventually found her luggage, and then spent almost an hour in a lineup at a customs desk to clear her bags. The terminal concourse was almost unbearably packed with meeters and greeters, but she eventually made her way to the doors of the glass-fronted building relatively unscathed and unmolested, except for a couple of quick anonymous clutches as she was getting out of the jetway and a clumsy attempt to unzip the bag on her hip and steal her wallet while she was emerging from customs. By the time she'd made her way through the crowds at customs and the even bigger throngs at immigration and finally reached the terminal exit, she'd paid out close to a hundred dollars American in "gratuities" and "fees" to half a dozen airport employees and officials.

When she stepped out of the building the heat hit her like a fist. So did the smell. On the ground the pollution was almost invisible, just a metallic haze in the distance, but the stink was just like the guy Hilts had said. It smelled like a giant litter box. Finn almost laughed out loud. All those years in school and it had come to this.

She looked around. There were people everywhere. Thousands of them. Tens of thousands of them, and they all seemed to know exactly where they were going. About half the men were wearing Western dress, while the other half wore a bewildering variety of the long flowing robes called *jelabia*. Some were turbaned, some wore small white embroidered skullcaps she knew were called *tagiyahs,* and others wore the Lawrence of Arabia-style *kafiya* with their braided silk-rope circlets. The women, dressed in skirts or in the more traditional robes, all had their heads covered, some only with scarves, while others were fully veiled. Her own copper-colored hair, tied back in a ponytail and barely covered by her battered old Toronto Blue Jays baseball cap, was drawing a lot of attention from the men, and none of it good.

Cars, trucks, minibuses, scooters, taxis, and tour busses crowded the curb. Horns blared, people yelled and gestured; there was even a horse-drawn cart with huge rubber wheels piled high with battered hubcaps. Finn found herself grinning broadly. It was hot as hell and blindingly sunny. The sounds were painfully loud and the traffic added its own sour smell to the air. It was a madhouse.

And it was wonderful.

With her carry-on in one hand and dragging a suit-case behind her, Finn threaded her way through the bustling crowd looking for the driver that had been promised. She'd been expecting an appropriately adven-turous Discovery Channel Toyota Land Cruiser, or better yet, a Land Rover. What she got was a distressingly rusted Fiat ambulance that at some stage in its long career had been converted into a minibus. Once upon a time the

Fiat had been red, but it had long since faded to pink. Finn could still see the almost invisible white cross on the door and the word 'emergency" along the side. Standing beside it was a young man in blue jeans, a skintight Shoenfelt T-shirt, and shiny Elvis Presley hair. He looked about sixteen, but she knew he had to be older than that. He was smoking a cigarette and clearly trying to look like Al Pacino in *Scarface*. He was carrying a cardboard sign that read ADAMSON EXPEDITION. Her smile widened even farther; it was amazing what that word "expedition" could do for your energy level after a long flight in a crowded airplane.

She humped her luggage across the broad sidewalk and crossed the street to the flat-nosed vehicle. "I'm Finn Ryan."

The young man gave a worldly sigh, breathing twin lines of smoke from his nostrils. He looked ridiculous. "Which one are you?"

"What do you mean?"

"What I said. Field Crew? Lab Crew? Volunteer? Specialist?" His English was perfect and nearly without accent.

"I'm the staff illustrator."

He nodded, looking her up and down. If he hadn't been so young she might have called it a leer. "Specialist."

"Who exactly are you?"

He made a sour face. "Achmed, the driver. Achmed, the translator. Achmed, the labor supervisor."

"I gather your name is Achmed."

"You couldn't pronounce my real name. Americans think all Egyptians are named Achmed, or Abdullah, or

6

Mohammed, so I'm Achmed. Achmed the Egyptian." He barked out a bitter little laugh.

Finn smiled. "What do Egyptians think all Americans are called?"

"In your case, *Ah'mar katha ath nan,*" Achmed replied, arching an eyebrow.

"Excuse me?"

"It means red-haired... sort of," said a voice behind her. It was Hilts, the dark-haired photographer from the plane. He was now wearing a battered pair of amber-tinted aviator-style Serengeti Drivers, a very old dark blue peaked cap with gold pilot wings embroidered on the band, and a cracked and ancient leather flying jacket that was far too heavy for the terrible heat. He smoked a fuming, slightly deformed cigarillo. His only luggage was a large gray canvas duffel bag with the name HILTS stenciled on the side.

"I'm Hilts," he said, leaning close to Achmed, then whispering, *"Balaak bennana derri lawTul'a!"*

Achmed's jaw dropped. *"Aawwaah!* You speak Dardja?"

Hilts rattled off another brief speech in the melodic, high-speed dialect, and the blood ran out of the young Egyptian's face. He muttered something to Finn, his eyes refusing to meet hers.

Hilts translated. "He apologizes for what he said and for offending you and he also begs your forgiveness."

"What did he say?"

"You don't want to know." He turned back to Achmed. "Why don't you put our bags on the bus?"

"Yes, of course, Mr. Hilts," Achmed said with a nod. He began loading the luggage.

"You're part of the expedition?" Finn asked, surprised.

"I told you, I'm a photographer."

"You look more like a flyer wearing that getup," she said, nodding at the cap and jacket.

"That too." He smiled. "I'm—"

"Don't tell me," Finn said and laughed, "you're an aerial photographer."

"You're quick for a girl."

They climbed into the minibus. Achmed got behind the wheel and they headed into the city. The drive into Cairo was a quick education in the art of automotive mayhem. There were thirteen million people living in Egypt's capital city, and by the looks of things all of them were in their cars and trying to get somewhere. Most of the vehicles were old and Japanese, Russian, or French, and the vast majority were missing at least one body part. All of them were blowing their horns. Red lights were ignored. There were no lanes of any kind and traffic cops were everywhere, having absolutely no effect on anything.

"Think like an autumn leaf floating on a fast-flowing river," Hilts cautioned philosophically as Achmed bullied his way into the city. "You'll eventually get there, but not necessarily by the route you intended or the speed you thought you'd be going."

The Nile Hilton was a late-50s monolithic slab and the first modern hotel built in Cairo. It sat like a giant pack of cigarettes blocking the view of the Nile on Midan Tahir, the overpopulated dead center of the city's financial district and the place where, one way or the other, all that traffic was headed. Achmed dropped them off at the Corniche El Nil entrance, dumped their bags on the sidewalk, and promised to be back in forty-eight hours to take them and the rest of the expedition to the civil airport in the Imbaba district on the other side of the river. The young man gave them a brief nod, slammed his door, and drove back into the seething traffic in a blast of exhaust, horn blaring.

"Welcome to Cairo," said Hilts. He helped Finn with her luggage and they checked in at the standard blonde oak and marble front desk. When they were done the pilot–photographer rode up with her in the elevator. "I'll meet you at Da Mario's in an hour," he said, getting out on his floor. "I need a lasagna fix."

"Da Mario's?"

"The best Italian food in Cairo. It's either that or Latex."

"Latex?"

"It's the hotel bar; very classy, believe it or not. They've got flavored vodka hookahs."

"I'll go for the lasagna."

"Good choice. Da Mario's, an hour." The door slid closed. Finn rode up another two floors, found her room, and dropped her bags at the end of the bed. She went to the balcony and stepped out. The sun was setting now and the western horizon was a streaked bloody fog of dying light. It was the most sinister, most dangerous, most beautiful thing she'd ever seen, like looking at the memory of a battle fought long ago, or a vision of one yet to come. She thought about where she would be going the day after tomorrow—out there, six thousand years of history waiting just around the corner. She stayed for a moment, then turned away, her heart beating hard with excitement. She went back into her room and began to unpack.

3

Da Mario's had old lamps, dark wood, and raffia-covered
Chianti bottles. Very Egyptian-looking waiters wandered
around with huge pepper grinders, inviting the guests to
have pepper on any and everything. Somebody in a dark
corner was playing "Che Sera, Sera" on a twelve-string
Spanish guitar. Hilts was sawing his way through a vast
plate of liberally peppered lasagna and Finn was working
on a small salad. They were sharing one of the raffia-
covered bottles of Chianti. Hilts was now wearing shorts
and a plain red T-shirt, while Finn had changed into jeans
and an NYU sweatshirt against the frigid air conditioning.

Finn took a bite of salad and shook her head. "My first
meal in Egypt and it winds up being something I could
get just as easily on Mulberry Street."

"We could go out to a local joint and get you some nice
bamya or maybe some *shakshukat beed iskandarani* if you
wanted something light, but you'd spend the next three
days on the toilet, if you'll pardon my French." He took
a sip of wine and then continued attacking his lasagna.
"The first rule about Egypt is don't ever drink the water.
The second is, don't ever eat the food."

"Is it really that bad?"

"It's not a question of bad, it's a question of acclimatiza-
tion. The tap water here is what they cook with, what they

mix their food with. Anything in the tap water is going to wind up in the food. They're used to the particular bugs, you're not. It's pretty simple."

"What about the dig?"

He shrugged. "You'll probably be sick as a dog for a couple of days. And they'll most likely boil the water. You'll be okay."

"The things my father never told me about the life of an archaeologist."

"You're L. A. Ryan's kid, right?"

"That's right. You knew him?"

"Knew of him. I resurveyed his original site in Mexico."

"The one in Yucatan? All I can really remember were the spiders. The size of dinner plates."

"That's the one. Quintana Roo. Chan Santa Cruz. It was the first time they ever had an infrared survey done. Tricky flying."

"You really have been everywhere."

He grinned. "I get around." His shoulders lifted and he took another sip of wine. "It's a job."

"What do you think about this one?"

"The job?" He shrugged again. I do know Rolf Adamson's a bit of a flake."

"All I read was the profile they did of him in *Newsweek* a while back. It's the only thing the library at school had on him."

"The reclusive billionaire thing?"

"I wonder how much of it's true," Finn said. "It made him sound like a cross between Bill Gates, Steven Spielberg, and Howard Hughes."

"With a little of the guy who owns Virgin Records thrown in for good measure. Balloon flights around the world, trips to the South Pole and all that."

"An adventurer who's interested in archaeology," said Finn. "Spending a million dollars financing a dig in the desert. He must have a serious side."

"According to my sources he's got a bee in his bonnet."

"Who are your sources and what kind of bee?"

"A lady on a dig he ran last year in Israel. They eventually took away his permits. Originally it had to do with one of those fake ossuaries that have been making the rounds. He tried to smuggle one out of the country and he got caught. It turned out to be one of the phonies, but that didn't change the intent. If he wants something he'll get it, no matter what the cost or whether it's legal or not."

"So what's the bee in his bonnet?"

"If you read the *Newsweek* profile you know who his grandfather was."

"Some kind of big-time evangelist from the twenties."

"Schuyler Grand. 'The Grand Army of God's Final Hour of Redemption.' They've written books about him. California's first radio evangelist. The ABN, Angel Broadcasting Network. Made millions and invested it all in orange groves and made millions more. Then he lost his radio license because everyone was saying he was secretly a Nazi. Committed suicide on the morning of Pearl Harbor. Adamson's tried to whitewash his reputation for years. Clear his name, resurrect his theories."

"What does that have to do with the dig?"

"Among other things, Schuyler Grand was an amateur archaeologist. He believed all the pseudo-science the

Nazis were spouting about master races, and he mixed it up with all sorts of other things, including the Holy Grail. His big pitch was that one of Christ's disciples carried the Grail to America."

"From what I was told we were digging up the remains of an old Coptic monastery at the Al-Kufrah oasis."

"We are. The Italians dug there in the late thirties. A guy named Lucio Pedrazzi. They were looking for the monastery too."

Finn smiled. "What aren't you telling me?"

"Officially this is a dig at a Coptic monastery. But I know for a fact Lucio Pedrazzi was digging for the tomb of a specific Coptic monk. A man named Didymus. In both Hebrew and Greek it means the same thing—'the twin.' Better known as Thomas the Apostle, or Doubting Thomas. Apparently Pedrazzi had evidence that after the Crucifixion Thomas went west, into the desert, rather than east, to India."

"It sounds like an Indiana Jones story."

"Pedrazzi was working for Mussolini's Italian Archaeology Mission in Libya. There's another story that says the monk in question wasn't Thomas at all. It was Christ himself, mysteriously disappeared from his own tomb with the help of a Roman legionary. Pedrazzi was trying to prove that the Roman legionary was part of the so-called Lost Legion. When Christ actually died years later the legion were in charge of his bones. They took them to some sort of lost city in the desert. According to Mussolini that gave him some sort of leverage with the Vatican. Crazy stuff. Pedrazzi disappeared in the middle of a sandstorm and was never seen again."

Finn looked skeptical. "I still don't see what any of this has to do with Rolf Adamson."

"Supposedly the legionary finally took the bones to America for safekeeping, which fits in with even more pseudoscientific stuff about ancient pyramids in Kansas and Egyptian galleys rowing down the Mississippi—after all, your average savage red Indian couldn't have built all those huge burial mounds, now could he? Racist horse crap, but lots of people believe it."

"And you think Adamson does?"

"I think Adamson's paying the freight. I'm a pragmatist. Jobs are scarce." He paused and took another sip of wine. He put down his glass and leaned against the back of the booth. "What about you?"

"Like you said, jobs are scarce." She fiddled with her own glass. "Besides, an adventure is an adventure."

"Which you seem to be in favor of."

"What do you mean?"

"Don't be bashful. How many Finn Ryans, daughter of renowned archaeologist Lyman Andrew Ryan, are there? You were all over the papers last year with that caper of yours under the streets of New York."

"It wasn't just me."

"No, it was you, the bastard son of a Pope of Rome, and the grandson of Mickey Hearts, your bigger-than-average New York mobster from the good old days. Not to mention a broad assortment of dead bodies and about a billion dollars' worth of looted art. And now you turn up here. Speaking of which, how exactly did you get the job?"

"I was recommended."

"By the young Mickey Hearts?"

14

Finn bristled. "His name is Michael Valentine and he's a book dealer, not a mobster. There is no mob anymore."

Hilts laughed. "Who told you that, your Mr. Valentine?" He shook his head. "You know that old story about the Devil—that the smartest thing he ever did was convince the world that he didn't exist? Pretty slick. Everybody talks about the Russians and the Japanese and the Hong Kong Triads but nobody talks about the Mafia anymore."

Finn was about to continue the argument but then saw the twinkle in Hilts's eye. "You're teasing me."

"Not really. Michael's a friend of mine too. He asked me to look out for you. He's not too happy about some of the people Rolf's involved with."

"You know Michael?" She could feel herself getting angry. She and Michael had briefly been lovers, but she didn't like the feeling that she was being patronized.

"We've done each other a few favors."

"I don't need a babysitter, Mr. Hilts."

"I don't intend to be one, Ms. Ryan. Michael just asked me to watch your back, that's all."

"I don't need that either."

"The desert's a big place, Finn. I could use a friend on this expedition myself." He held a hand out across the table. "Peace?"

Finn hesitated for a moment, then shrugged. She valued her independence, but she'd also learned the hard lesson that there was sometimes strength in numbers. A friend in a strange land like this couldn't do any harm. She shook the offered hand. "Peace." She went back to her salad for a moment as Hilts finished his meal. "So when do we meet our benefactor?"

"He's already on-site. We're waiting for a late addition to the group and then I fly us out to Al–Kufrah the day after tomorrow."

"Who's the mystery guest?"

"A Frenchman named Laval. He's a specialist in Coptic inscriptions from l'École Biblique in Jerusalem."

"A priest?"

"A monk."

"Could be interesting."

"Could be very interesting," said Hilts. "There was a monk from the same school on Pedrazzi's expedition back in the thirties. A man named DeVaux. He was with Pedrazzi when he disappeared. Maybe this guy Laval is interested in more than just scrawls on a wall."

Finn laughed. "How do you know all this stuff?"

"I like to know who I'm working with and I've got a lot of time to read on long flights." He cocked an eyebrow. "And I'm also an amateur conspiracy theorist. Show me a mystery and I'll connect it to the disappearance of Jimmy Hoffa and the Kennedy assassination."

"When does the mystery monk arrive?"

"Late tomorrow night."

"I guess I can play tourist for one day."

"I'm doing a photostory for *National Geographic Traveler*. Why don't you come along?"

"Where are you going?"

"The City of the Dead. The liveliest cemetery in the world. You'll love it."

4

In the immense, ancient, and melodramatic sprawl that is the city of Cairo, there are five major cemeteries that were once located on the eastern edges of the city beneath the Muqattam Hills, but which had been absorbed by the ever-growing metropolis many years before. In the old way, in a time when the family of the departed would mourn beside the grave for forty days and nights, the tombs for even the most modestly endowed were provided with small shelters for the living, while great mosques and death houses were built by the rich and the important. Streets and alleys between and around the graves and monuments appeared, and eventually the five cemeteries beneath the hills became known as the City of the Dead. In the second half of the twentieth century overcrowding, immense poverty, and a population that grew by a thousand a day forced the living into the confines of the dead. Over the years a city within a city grew until the cemeteries were occupied by more than a million desperate souls, all of them surviving without heat, electricity, or sanitation.

It was Friday, the Muslim holy day, and the streets of Cairo were almost empty of traffic, a nearly miraculous change from Finn's arrival. She waited under the shaded entrance to the hotel, looking out across the square. On the left was the old Museum of Antiquities, already under siege by the occupants of a dozen tour busses parked out front. To the right was the sand-colored slab of the Arab League headquarters, and directly across the square was the entrance to the Cairo Bus Station.

Following Hilts's advice about local customs, Finn had dressed carefully, wearing loose linen pants and an equally unrevealing green silk top. She'd tied her hair back in a scarf, hiding everything, including her bangs. She wore a plain pair of North Face hiking boots and her favorite drugstore sunglasses. She'd left her passport with the front desk, had nothing but her international driver's license for ID, and carried only five hundred Egyptian pounds, less than a hundred dollars. She'd left her digital camera locked in her suitcase under the bed and picked up a disposable Fuji in the hotel gift shop. According to Hilts, the trick about a trip to the City of the Dead was to make sure you didn't appear to be worth mugging, raping, or killing.

A thundering roar broke into the relative peace of the morning and Finn saw a huge black motorcycle turn into the square from the Nile side and rumble toward the hotel entrance. The rider stopped directly in front of her and pulled off his dark, full-visor helmet. It was Hilts. He was wearing motorcycle boots, jeans, and a T-shirt that read "Harley-Davidson Egypt" on the front. The name on the side of the motorcycle spelled out Norton. He reached back and handed Finn a helmet.

"Hop on."

"I thought we were supposed to be keeping a low profile."

"Sometimes fun takes precedence over good sense. I don't get to ride bikes much anymore."

"You're crazy," she said, slipping on the helmet and buttoning the chin strap. Suddenly the world was the amber color of the visor.

"That too," he said and grinned. She climbed on the bike behind him, put her arms around his waist, and they were off.

5

They rode through the smoky fog of pollution along the Corniche El Nil, then turned away from the river and the Island of Rhoda along the wide and almost empty Salah Salim highway. To the right was vacant waste ground and abandoned building sites; to the left was Telal Zenhom, a district ravaged by the massive earthquake in 1992. It was all like some sort of arid *Blade Runner*. Heavy electrical cables ran like thick black snakes across rooftops and TV antennas drooped from minarets.

They turned off Salah Salim at the Al-Qadiraya exit and slowed as they moved steadily deeper into the intricate web of roads and alleys that made up the crumbling, foul-smelling necropolis. Within seconds Finn was completely disoriented, lost in a sea of tombs and tombstones.

They stopped. Ahead of them was a broad circular mosque, teardrop-shaped windows exquisitely carved into the old white stone. To one side of the mosque, built on the roof of a large, thick-walled death house, was a ramshackle assembly of crates and boxes, looking more like a chicken coop than a place suitable for human habitation. Finn climbed off the motorcycle and slid her helmet off. Instantly her eyes began to sting. Here the pollution was even heavier, made worse by a thick, clinging fog of gray-white dust that began to clog her nose and mouth.

Hilts reached into the pouch at his waist, took out a surgical mask and handed it to her. She slipped it on gratefully.

Hilts dug out a second mask and put it on. "Living in Cairo is the equivalent of smoking a pack and a half of cigarettes a day."

"Camels?" Finn responded.

"Very funny. Keep the mask on." He clipped his helmet onto the rear carrier rack and did the same with Finn's. A crowd of children, all boys of varying sizes and ages, had gathered around them. They stared silently at the two Americans.

"What do they want?" Finn asked.

"Anything you've got," Hilts replied. "They're beggars."

But these kids weren't the jostling innocent ragamuffins she had seen in movies, hands outstretched for a few coins. This was a feral pack of young wolves, eyes dark and full of hate for anyone who had more than them, which was virtually anyone else in the world. One of them, the tallest, wore a soiled skullcap, a torn pair of shorts, and a faded pink "Feelin' Lucky" Care Bears T-shirt. Like everything else he was covered with a layer of thin, streaked gray dust. He had one hand thrust deeply into the pocket of his shorts. In the other hand he carried a fist-sized chunk of rubble.

"Shu ismaq?" asked Hilts, taking a step forward.

"Baqir," the boy replied, hefting the rock.

"Lovely," muttered Hilts.

"What?"

"Baqir is his name. It means 'to rip open' in Arabic."

"Are we in trouble?"

"I could always let them kidnap you, then run like hell."

"I'm serious," said Finn.

"So am I," said Hilts, but she could see him smiling behind the mask. He reached into the pocket of his jeans and flipped two coins at the boy, one after the other. He caught them both, but he had to drop the rock to manage it. Hilts spoke to him again in Arabic and the boy nodded. *"Shukran,"* Hilts said, bowing slightly. "That's thank you," he added for Finn's benefit. "A good word to remember. That and *saadni!"*

"What does *sadnii* mean?" Finn asked, struggling with the pronunciation.

"Help me!"

Hilts opened the saddlebag slung across the rear baggage rack and took out an identical pair of old and well-used Nikon F3s. He slung the cameras over his shoulder, then took Finn by the elbow and led her away from the crowd of boys, who now surrounded the motor-cycle.

"You're just leaving the bike there?" Finn asked, startled.

"I gave him fifty piastre. That's about a dime. I promised him five pounds if he watched it until we got back. That's about a buck. More than he earns in a whole day on the streets unless he's a tourist *sariq*—a pickpocket."

"You trust him?"

"I put the fear of god into him. He knows who the bike belongs to."

"And that would be who?"

"A friend of mine who operates a dealership on Zamalek, that's the big island in the middle of the Nile you can see from your hotel balcony. She has six brothers."

"Who are they?" Finn asked, already seeing where the conversation was going.

"Boukoloi," said Hilts. "Bandits. The most powerful gang of bandits in Cairo."

"Bandits. Sounds romantic."

"Depends on how you look at it. There's not a lot of violent crime in Egypt if you don't count traffic accidents, but Cairo is a major transit point for heroin from Southeast Asia on its way to Europe and the States. Conflict diamonds come through here out of Sierra Leone to Antwerp. The Nigerians use Cairo as a money laundry on a huge scale. The software piracy rate is almost seventy percent. On top of that there's a billion-dollar-a-year industry in the smuggling of stolen artifacts, not to mention the fifty thousand pickpockets and the hundred thousand petty thieves."

"So our friend Baqir back there knows who these *boukoloi* are?"

"He's probably on the payroll. His parents are most likely funeral merchants, if he has parents."

"What's a funeral merchant?"

"A new age grave robber. Somebody, a door-man, a cop, a neighbor hears about someone dying and they get in touch with a funeral merchant. A gang of kids like Baqir go to wherever the person lived and strip the place clean, sometimes before the next of kin has been notified. Most of the clothes for sale in the *suqs*, the markets here, have come off dead bodies."

"Gross."

"The Muslims have a closer relationship with their dead than Christians do. They revere their ancestors, even love them. They don't try to bury them and forget them. Not to mention the fact that it's practical." They stopped at a rough stall made by hanging a piece of ragged cloth between two granite crypts. A veiled woman squatted in the dust, a selection of clothes in front of her. Hilts spoke to her briefly, then used one of the Nikons to take her photograph. He knelt down and picked up a fleece-lined shirt that looked almost brand-new. He asked the veiled woman the price and she told him. "A pound," he said to Finn. "Twenty cents. I could barter with her and get it for half that."

Finn sniffed the shirt. It had a sickly sweet odor. "Is that what I think it is?"

"Sometimes they don't get to the dead people for a day or two. He was probably wearing it when he died."

"Not your size," said Finn. Hilts put the shirt down and they moved on, making their way deeper and deeper into the labyrinth. The crowds got denser and denser as they continued, the swirling dust half-blinding and the continuous babbling crush of noise assaulting their ears.

There were piles of broken toys, smashed remote controls, old plastic containers, typewriters, VCRs, and dented hubcaps. The larger used clothing vendors had their goods piled into mountains laid out on sheets of grimy plastic. Almost everything looked American, and people pored over the heaps of clothing like flies holding up blouses, underwear, pants, ties, shorts, T-shirts, and socks, haggling for price, sometimes buying, most often moving on.

"You know those big bins of used clothes you see in some city neighborhoods, usually at a strip mall?" Hilts asked. Finn nodded. "This is where they wind up. The so-called charities you think you're giving stuff to sell it by the ton to third world brokers, and they sell it to people like this."

A ragged man sitting on a stool in front of a display of shoes called out in surprisingly good English, yelling to make himself heard over the never-ending din, "American lady! Julia Roberts! I have shoes for you."

Finn paused. The shoes were all men's. The vendor held one up. It looked like a size-twelve side-zipped suede boot from the sixties. There was only one. "There's only one," she pointed out.

The vendor held up another shoe. A much smaller loafer. "They are both black." The man smiled. His teeth were the color of wet cigarette butts.

"But they don't match."

"I give you deal. Half price for one," the would-be shoe salesman cackled. "I love you, Miss Julia Roberts!" he called after them.

They turned a corner and went down a short alley to another main pathway between the plaster tombs and rows of raised sarcophagi.

"The animal market," said Hilts. "It can get pretty ugly here."

There was a sudden gust of wind and Finn squinted into the small hurricane of blowing dust. She blinked and cleared her throat and blinked again, her eyes watering. She smelled the market before she saw it, a rank sweet scent of death and offal that cut through the ever-present stink of rotting garbage and raw sewage that flowed along the narrow gutters. She heard the market as well, a mad mixture of sheep and goats and snuffling pigs and crowing roosters. Dogs barked and monkeys chattered.

A woman brushed by her carrying a large blue crate that read "Wal-Mart" on the side. Finn glanced at the woman's wares and gagged. The bin was filled with animal organs and intestines swimming in a soup of blood and other fluids. Off to the side she saw a huge cage of desert tortoises piled one on top of the other, hundreds of them, the ones on the bottom crushed by the weight of those above.

Beside that was an old glass-sided display cabinet full of snakes, some as thick as an infant's arm, motionless, stunned by the heat and haze and noise, far from their natural habitats far down the Nile. A little farther on Finn looked down a narrow alley and saw children playing some sort of jumping game around a scarecrow figure standing rooted to a patch of weeds. The scarecrow was dressed in a dark blue velvet smoking jacket and the striped pants from an old morning suit. On its head was a dreadlock wig, and on the wig an old tweed cap. Looking closer Finn saw that the clothes were hanging on a desiccated corpse wired to a metal pole, the dirt-brown creature's skeleton still held together by dried ropes of leathery tendon and muscle. The face of the scarecrow was black and rotted. Finn looked away.

"You okay?" Hilts asked.

Finn swallowed the taste of bile in the back of her throat then nodded. "I'm fine," she answered.

Beyond the meat market, in a courtyard bounded by three plain crypts, was a taxidermy display with stuffed versions of some of the same animals they'd seen a few yards away, diabolical with glass eyes stripped from dolls, evil grins filled with bared teeth and fangs, strange hybrids, geese with fox ears, dogs with grafted monkey heads, bright parrots with outstretched eagles' wings.

"Who buys this stuff?"

"In a city as large as this there's a buyer for everything," Hilts said and shrugged. He grinned. "New York with pyramids." The crowd was pressing them forward like pieces of driftwood on the tide, but Hilts steadily moved them off to one side.

"Where to now?" Finn asked.

"There," he answered, pointing. Down an alley she could see yet another opening and more piles of merchandise. Most of it appeared to be military—gas masks, empty mortar shells, ancient range finders, at least a hundred pair of World War Two desert boots, gasoline cans, even a small cannon, its muzzle shattered, a relic of some long-forgotten battle.

Hilts slipped into the narrow alley ahead of Finn, separated from her for a moment. A gray-haired beggar, burnt brown by the sun, hopped in front of her, staggering on a bright pink artificial leg, his hand outstretched, screaming into her face in unintelligible Arabic, his face twisted into a furious mask. She backed away, but there was no place to move, the crowd behind shoving her out of the way, forcing her down an even narrower side passage. Suddenly Hilts was gone and she was alone.

6

She realized that she had been thrust completely out of the market; there were no piles of merchandise or haggling crowds. In an instant she found herself taken into a different world, a world of crumbling walls, of huddled figures in the swirling dust, of a strange silence, the noise of the crowd immediately muffled by the thick plaster walls of the death houses all around her, the light turned to flitting shadows. Her fear was instantaneous.

She stood still, turning slowly in a circle, trying to get her bearings. In front of her was a high wall made of mud bricks and straw, worn in places, some bricks gone, like missing teeth. To her left was a pale green building with a sloping roof, and to the right was a narrow alley barely wide enough to slip through sideways. Behind her was the path leading back to the street she had been ejected from.

Finn turned back that way. She knew Hilts had been heading toward the wider area of old military surplus. If she hurried she would probably be able to catch up. She pelted through the opening and then pulled up short. A man stood before her, dressed in a white jelabia and a dark, pin-striped suit jacket. His feet were bare and his head was wrapped in a loose, filthy turban.

He looked as though he was in his forties, slope-shouldered and big-chested. His eyes were yellow green and sunk deep under heavy brows, his nose large, flattened and twisted from several obvious breaks, his upper lip and chin covered by a graying beard. Like everything else in the City of the Dead, he was covered in a thin film of dust.

In one large hand he held a huge leaf-shaped sword, the blade pitted with rust, the edge hard and shining from a recent sharpening. He raised the machete-like blade and opened his mouth wide, making a gargling, growling sound, revealing that he had no tongue within his black, stained mouth.

For a frozen instant Finn stood stock-still, simply staring. She felt a panic-stricken laugh burst from her lips and for a second all she could think about was the scene in the Indiana Jones film where Harrison Ford faced a giant Egyptian swordsman of his own. It was ridiculous, but it was horribly real. She wasn't Indiana Jones and she had no big horse pistol to shoot down the grotesque creature swinging the blade in her direction. The man grunted a second time and then surged forward. Finn spun on her heels and ran.

Racing back out of the narrow alley, she swung instinctively to the left, running beside the crumbling brick wall, then turned the corner to the right and ran on, hearing the pounding feet of her terrifying pursuer close behind. She scanned the way ahead. She was in a small open space surrounded by the walls of large stone mausoleums, doors and windows heavily grated against any intrusion.

In the square were a dozen stone slabs marking simpler burial plots. A cooking fire burned on one of them, a pot hanging by a metal hook above the embers. Finn ran forward into the middle of the empty courtyard, jumped up on the slab, and spun toward the fire.

Half turning, she grabbed the steaming pot by the handle and swung it backward, kicking through the hot coals and spreading them all over the slab. The iron pot of *kohary* splashed across the big man's face, momentarily blinding him in a mess of boiling-hot slushy rice and lentils.

He yelled and pawed at his face with his free hand and jumped onto the stone slab as Finn slipped, then fell, rolling into the dirt. The man raised the machete and stepped forward, the skin of his bare feet treading on a spray of white coals. He howled and jerked back, falling sideways into the remains of the fire. Finn regained her feet and kept on running, not daring to look back to see what damage she had done.

She threw herself into a narrow crack between two of the mausoleums and came out into a small alley. Directly in front of her she saw an open doorway, a cool dark haven from the man behind her. She ran into the modest death house. Laid out on the bare earth floor, only half covered by dust and dirt, were three skeletons in a neat row, feet all pointing in one direction, probably the east, although Finn no longer had any idea which way was which.

It looked as though someone had been to the simple grave site recently. There were spade marks in the dirt, as though someone had been excavating. There was no archaeology going on here though; if the skeletons had been disinterred it was because the living wanted to move into the rough shelter of the simple one-room building.

There was a second opening on the other side of the room, and stepping over the skeletons in the dirt, Finn exited into a broad enclosure of two or three dozen graves out in the open with rows of smaller chambers on either side and the high wall of what Finn took to be a mosque at the far end. There were picks and sledgehammers lying around and piles of broken marble and granite slabs: grave robbers stealing the actual graves themselves, the descendants of Saladin's builders who stripped the pyramids of their smooth outer facings to raise the city.

She stopped just outside the death house and listened, trying to slow her breathing and the rattletrap beating of her heart. As far as she could tell the man with the machete and no tongue was no longer after her. Either that or he was being a lot quieter about it. The real question of course was why he had been after her in the first place. She was a woman in a strange place, and alone at that, but unless the lunatic sword wielder simply wandered around the City of the Dead looking for damsels in distress, he was after her for a reason.

For the life of her though she couldn't figure out what possible reason there could be. Her recent exploits in the shady world of looted art, old conspiracies, and Vatican politics didn't have anything at all to do with Egypt; the works of art she'd managed to unearth, literally, from beneath the streets of New York hadn't included any Rosetta Stones or pharaohs' treasures. And even if they had, who would want to kill her now? That part of her life was over.

Or was it?

If she was right the man with the machete had been waiting for her like a hunter waiting to stalk his prey. That meant he had to have known she was coming to the City of the Dead today, and the only person who knew that other than herself was Hilts—a man who had introduced himself to her on an airplane, a man who had said he was part of the expedition but who had only offered his name to Achmed the driver. And who, for that matter, was Achmed, except a young man holding a sign that said "Adamson"?

She had taken it all on faith. As her friend Michael Valentine would have told her, the essence of any good confidence trick was just that, a trick of confidence, depending on the victim's faith that what he or she was seeing was true because it was what was expected. Hilts knowing who she was, her background, her father's name and reputation, Michael's background… all of it was readily available in the archives of any major newspaper that had carried the story a year ago, or on the Internet. She'd fallen for it hook, line and sinker, believed it because she wanted to, because Hilts was a good-looking, intelligent man with a ready smile and an interesting patter.

Finn swore under her breath. She'd gotten herself into this mess; now she had to get herself out. She quickly looked around the narrow enclosed area once again. A rough ladder made from old lumber leaned up against the right-hand death house. Height. Maybe she could figure out where she was if she got high enough. It was worth a try.

She ran across the enclosure, threading her way between the graves, and climbed the ladder. She reached the top of the mud-and-plaster building and went to the far edge. Stretching out in all directions was a mazelike sea of buildings just like the one she stood on, split by alleys and paths. Some were so close they shared walls, others were separated like the enclosure behind her. The lower buildings were punctuated here and there with larger ones, some two stories high or even three, with taller, more ornate mosques rising out of the crumbling sea of brick and stone.

In the far distance she could see the palacelike bulk of the Citadel, built on a spur of limestone that dominated the city a thousand years ago as the Dome of the Winds by Sultan Hatim Ibn Hartama, then brutally fortified by Saladin two hundred years later as a royal seat and fortress for himself and future Abbasid rulers. Between the Citadel and where she now stood she could see a raised highway that seemed to cut directly across the City of the Dead. She could also see something else: just to the right, two hundred yards away, was a small round mosque with windows cut like teardrops. Beside it, in stark contrast to the mosque's beauty, was a squalid hovel built of chicken wire and lumber scraps. It was the mosque she'd seen getting off the motorcycle. Somewhere in the shadows and the bleak, mustard-and-ash haze below it was Baqir and his horde of child bandits. No match for the machete-swinging thug behind her, but better than nothing. She turned and went back to the ladder.

She stooped, ducking low. Her nightmarish adversary was now directly below her, scanning the little enclosure. There were several ways she could have gone, but for the moment he hadn't thought of looking up. His robe was charred along one edge and he was limping. It looked as though she had slowed him a little. He was making soft, animal noises, head slowly turning as he examined the area. Finn edged back, trying to get out of his potential line of sight should he suddenly look upward. Her foot sagged into a soft spot in the roof and a chunk of mortar or brick dropped down noisily into the room below. Instantly the man's eyes flashed up. Finn didn't wait. She turned and ran, heading for the far edge of the roof as the man with the machete began to climb the ladder, bellowing with rage or pain or both.

Finn reached the far side of the small building, paused, lurched then launched herself across the five-foot gap, landing hard on the next roof, the gravelly surface tearing at the palms of her hands and shredding the knees of her linen pants. She rolled upright and saw the son of a bitch with the sword in his hand stumbling across the far roof, one foot dragging. She looked ahead and to the sides. The next roof was closer, so she ran toward it and jumped the narrower gap easily, trying to keep herself lined up with the round mosque.

She leapt over a low parapet between two adjoining death houses and kept on going, feeling her breath hot and desperate pumping from her burning lungs. She turned for an instant and gasped out loud. Somehow the swordsman had managed to drastically shorten the distance between them, limp and all. Reaching the edge of the roof she stopped, horrified. It was twenty feet across open air to the next roof and fifteen feet to the ground. Below her was a bare patch of earth and several crumbling gravestones. Someone had arranged a scrap of cloth between poles to create a makeshift awning. She had no choice. She jumped, aiming for the sagging cloth.

Finn dropped, turning her shoulder with the fall. She crashed through the ragged piece of fabric and splintered the frail structure that held it up. A woman screamed, and there was a second crash as the few pots and pans that made up the kitchen Finn had just demolished clattered to the ground. Finn had a quick impression of a shrouded woman carrying a naked, wide-eyed child, and just beyond a piece of billboard with a line of Arabic script and the English word "Dreamland" in bright orange type.

Directly above her she heard a guttural roar, and suddenly the swordsman dropped the wreckage of the woman's awning and stood in front of her, legs spread wide, the huge blade raised in his arms. He grunted out some incoherent oath and charged. Finn grabbed a tattered piece of the awning and pulled it downward into the man's face, confusing him for a split second. To the left, on a raised stone coffin, were the plucked and gutted corpses of half a dozen pigeons, their ruffed heads severed at the neck and piled beside the bodies in a heap, eyes glazed, beaks wide. The cleaver that had done the job lay nearby, the blade still sticky with blood. Off to the side a green buzzing cloud of shiny-winged flies danced above a small wooden bowl that was filled with the small creatures' entrails. Reaching out, Finn grabbed the cleaver and swung it blindly, feeling the heavy jolt as the blade cut into flesh and slid hard across bone. A strange high-pitched scream rose into the dense, filthy air, and Finn ran again.

She turned out of the small corner of abandoned ground she had tumbled into and found herself in a long, dark alleyway, a blank wall rising up in front of her like a cliff. Looking up she saw the familiar tear-shaped windows, with the chicken coop structure just visible on the right. The high wall had to be the rear of the mosque near the motorcycle.

Behind her she could hear the pounding of the swordsman's bare feet on the path and his labored breathing, but she didn't even try to look back. Instead she tried to run faster, eyes moving to the left and right. There was no door at the end of the dark, narrow passage, no ladders or opening to the side, no way out. It was a dead end. There was nowhere else to run, no other option except to turn and make a futile stand that could only end in savage pain and final oblivion.

The one faint hope was a window in the wall of the mosque, but as she continued to run forward she saw that it was much too high to reach. Besides, it was covered with an ornately carved and decorated wooden screen. It was no use, she was as good as dead. She looked on the ground in front of her, desperately hoping to find something she could use as a weapon, but there was nothing except hard bare ground and the ever-present layer of dust.

She hesitated, half turning to meet her fate, then turned back to the mosque, seeing a movement and a flash of color on the periphery of her vision. There was a crash and the wooden screen that blocked the high window shattered outward and a figure in a pink T-shirt appeared.

Baqir, the Care Bear bandit.

The boy yelled something incomprehensible in Arabic and leaned out of the window, extending both arms down the pale wall of the mosque. Beyond him Finn could see several of his young companions, anchoring him from behind. In a last frantic burst she reached the foot of the wall and jumped, clutching for the boy's outstretched hands. She felt him grip her wrists and drag her upward. From behind her came a rush of air and the clattering smash of steel on stone as the swordsman hacked upward with his blade, missing the stroke, the machete biting into the wall instead of her flesh.

Baqir and his gang hauled Finn through the broken window and into the cool semidarkness of the mosque. They were on a raised gallery edged with more wooden screens like the one that had covered the window. Below was an empty prayer space covered with beautifully woven carpets facing a tall altarlike structure. Above there was nothing but the yawning emptiness of the dome, the arching barrel of the vault decorated in fantastic, complex mosaics of tile in blues, greens, and gold, like the sun shining down on the fields and streams of paradise.

Baqir and his friends pulled her toward a narrow flight of steps, then hurried her across the carpet-covered floor to an arched doorway on the other side of the high, open space. They headed out into the smoky haze. Ahead, two young boys were playing marbles on a gravestone. Baqir barked an order. The marble players looked up, replied quickly, then ran off. One of Baqir's shorter lieutenants tugged at Finn's sleeve and gestured with a word. They moved quickly down a broad pathway and through an old wrought-iron gate that led out into a surprisingly green garden of flowers growing in front of a small but obviously prosperous mausoleum, its walls freshly whitewashed, its windows covered with ornate wooden grilles.

Led by her crowing, chattering escort Finn raced down a narrow alley then burst out into a wider area bounded by more gravestones and awning-covered areas of shade like the one she'd crashed through a few moments before. It was another version of the animal market. The stench was almost overpowering. In one corner a rough table was stacked with what Finn knew had to be freshly butchered camel legs, lumps of yellow bone protruding from severed flesh and blood-clotted fur. Buckets were lined up, filled with goat, donkey, and sheep entrails. Old jars, tins, and drums stuffed with overflowing slabs of cow liver and raw fat sat cooking in the roasting sun. A hundred people crowded into a space no bigger than a couple of ordinary parking spaces.

"Ya'la! Ya'la!" a little boy beside her yelled, dragging her across the market. Small hands pushed her from behind, and ahead Baqir scouted the next alley. Less than a minute later, gasping and exhausted, Finn stumbled out into the court where she and Hilts had left the Norton. Baqir, grinning broadly, eyes flashing, pumped his fist triumphantly into the air. Finn made her way over to the bike and leaned on it, chest heaving. Relief welled up in her with a wracking sob. Suddenly her new sidekick screamed.

"Shoef!"

She turned in time to see the gleaming arc of the machete cutting through the air and slicing into Baqir's neck at the shoulder, butchering down through muscle, bone, and heart. The light went out in the young thief's eyes before he knew what was happening, and he fell dead to the dusty ground. The swordsman slid the blade away from the crumpled body, smiling hugely. His own blood was heavy on the upper arm of his old morning coat, his dark eyes blazing.

He grunted something loudly that sounded like *"Kus umak!"* and began to stride toward her as best he could, dragging his right foot and swinging the bloody machete like a club. Baqir's gang fled, screaming in terror as the ghastly apparition moved steadily forward—all except Finn's little protector, who stood loyally beside her, visibly shaking, his small hand on her sleeve. The child took one step forward and spit onto the ground. He swore at the swordsman in a squeaking voice, bent down, and hurled a chunk of rubble.

"*Sharmut!*" shrieked the little boy, tears of rage streaking through the caked dirt and grime on his face.

The piece of rock struck the man on his uninjured shoulder and bounced off harmlessly. Smiling, he came on. Finn grabbed the child and pulled him back, forcing him behind her. The man raised the machete, Baqir's glistening blood dripping from the blade down onto his hand. Finn's heart seemed to stop beating and she felt a calm, deadly coldness overtake her. She saw Baqir falling into the dirt again like some useless thing, abandoned. The grotesque creature with the bleeding sword in his hand would pay. She searched the terrible face approaching her, wondering if there was any hope that she could use her teeth to rip out his throat before she died.

"*W'aleikum sallam.*" The words were soft, and close. The man with the machete in his hand stopped, surprised by the voice. He turned slightly, so that the three closely spaced rounds struck him high in the ribs. The bullets shattered the curved bones guarding his chest into a hundred spiked, razorlike fragments that tore through both lungs and heart, lifting the man off his feet, tossing him backward like a rag. Two of the three bullets ricocheting through the meat of his chest finally found their way out of his body, exploding through the right shoulder blade and blowing out the center of his spine in a misty halo of blood and bone and scraps of fabric from the old, pin-striped morning coat. The dead swordsman's body hit the ground with a sound like a heavy sack of turnips dropping on the dirt.

Finn looked. Hilts stood there for an instant longer, the small square shape of the South African RAP automatic held outward at arm's length, gripped firmly in a simple one-handed grip with no theatrics. The moment passed and he flipped up the safety, then stuffed the weapon into his waistband and covered it with his T-shirt.

He bent, quickly scooping up the three .40-caliber shell casings and pushing them into his pocket. In three steps he was beside the motorcycle. He took a folded wad of Egyptian pounds out of his jeans and pressed them into the hands of the little boy still standing with Finn, staring at the blasted swordsman with childish awe. He squeezed the boy's hand tightly around the money, then whispered briefly into his ear. The child stared up at Hilts and nodded. The money vanished beneath his ragged, dirty robe.

"*Imshee, imshee!*" said Hilts. The boy looked quickly up at Finn, tears still hot in his eyes, then kissed her hand and ran. The child stopped for an instant beside the dead swordsman, kicked dirt onto his face and spit, then clutched the blood-soaked handle of the machete and dragged it away with him, leaving a thin, telltale trace as the point furrowed through the hard-packed earth. In the distance Finn could hear the faint sounds of whistles blowing.

"We've got to get out of here," said Hilts. He pushed his two Nikons into the carrier bag, handed over Finn's helmet and slipped on his own. He swung onto the motorcycle. "Come on."

Finn climbed on behind him. The sirens were closer now. "Tell me how to say 'thank you' again," she said quietly.

40

"*Shukran*," Hilts answered.

She looked at the frail young body of Baqir, sprawled in the dirt. A huge pool of dusty blood surrounded his head and shoulders, and already the flies were gathering.

"*Shukran*, Baqir," she whispered softly, and pulled down her visor. Hilts fired up the engine, revved it once, and then they raced away, leaving the City of the Dead behind them.

7

Hilts delivered the Norton back to its owner then walked back along the tree-shaded street to where he'd dropped Finn off at the Hotel Longchamps. She sat at a secluded table in one corner of the second-floor terrace, sipping a cup of American coffee and looking out over the upscale neighborhood on the island of Zamalek. Here there was nothing of the terrible scenes she had just witnessed. No crowds, no haze of choking dust, just the quiet movement of traffic on the pleasant street below, the rustle of a breeze in the trees and a distant glimpse of the river a few blocks away. It could just as easily have been somewhere in Westchester or Mount Vernon. The City of the Dead was nothing more than a distant whispered nightmare in a place like this. Beside her, Hilts sat down, his eyes hidden behind his sunglasses. He ordered a tall glass of iced tea and then ignored it for a long while.

Finn spoke at last. "I just saw a little boy murdered and I saw you shoot a man to death and you made it look like target practice. You made it look as though it wasn't the first time. The police are looking for whoever killed that man and I'm involved and I want to know just what the hell is going on."

"I'm not sure."

"What about that man who was chasing after me? Who was he?"

"I don't know."

"He couldn't have known I'd be there unless you told him."

"I never saw him before. All I know is that one of Baqir's kids found me and told me you were in trouble and I came after you."

"With a gun."

"That's right, with a gun."

"Explain that."

"That's why I went to the City of the Dead in the first place. It's not as easy as it used to be to just put a handgun in your luggage and bring it through customs."

"I thought you were there to take pictures."

"I was."

"So if I phoned *National Geographic* they'd know what I was talking about."

"Talk to a guy named Russ Tamblyn."

"You still haven't explained about the gun."

"It was necessary."

"Why?"

"Because I don't trust Adamson for one thing, and I don't like our so-called liaison with the Libyan government."

"Who's that?"

"A man named Mustapha Hisnawi. He's supposed to be some kind of archaeologist, but from what I hear he's also a full-tilt colonel in the *Haiat amn al Jamahiriya*: the Jamahiriya Security Organization. The Libyan Secret Police."

"Where do you come by that kind of information?"

43

"I've got a lot of friends, and like I told you, I read a lot."

"You seem to shoot a lot too."

"From time to time."

"Where did you learn that particular skill? Not from reading books."

"Boy Scouts."

"Oh, sure."

"It's true. I got a merit badge. I was also in the marines for a few years."

"I'm not sure I believe any of this."

"Believe what you like. All I know is that guy looked like he was about to chop you in half."

"And instead he chopped Baqir in half."

"I was too late. I'm sorry about that. I would give anything to have been able to prevent that."

"Maybe you wouldn't have to be sorry if you hadn't gone there looking for a gun."

"Maybe, maybe not."

"How can you be that callous? A child is dead."

"I didn't kill him, that son of a bitch with the sword did. A son of a bitch who was chasing you, I might add, not me."

"Which brings me back to my original point—why would he be chasing me?"

"Something to do with the expedition?"

"Like what? I'm supposed to be a technical illustrator and cartographer. I'll be drawing site diagrams and artifacts. It's not like it's very high up the ladder."

"Some old enemy?"

"I don't have any enemies like that."

Hilts thought for a moment. "Who hired you?"

44

"Adamson's office in California."

"Was there an interview?"

"Over the phone. The placement office at NYU sent them a bunch of possibles. They short-listed me, I sent in my résumé along with a list of references, and then I had a five-minute phone interview."

"Who did you talk to?"

"A guy named Forrest, one of Adamson's personnel people."

"Same person who hired me."

"Is it important?"

"I don't know."

"I don't like mysteries."

"Neither do I."

"So why was the guy after me?" She shook her head. "He must have been following us for quite a while. As soon as you and I got separated he was onto me. As though he'd been waiting for me."

"That's impossible. No one knew we were coming."

"So you say." Finn shrugged.

"I'm lying?"

"How do I know you're telling the truth?"

"Why would I lie?" he answered.

"I don't think this is going to get us anywhere."

"Apparently not." They fell into a long silence. Finally Hilts spoke again. "Aliyah," he said, nodding to himself.

"What?"

"Not what, who. Aliyah is the woman I borrowed the motorcycle from. She was the one who told me where to find a gun in the City of the Dead. She knew where I was going."

"You think she told somebody?"

"I can't think of anyone else."

"Why would she do something like that?"

He grimaced. "For money. It's the only reason she does anything."

"On whose behalf?"

"Adamson's?"

"He hires us, then he kills us?" Finn shook her head. "That doesn't make any sense. And it still doesn't explain why that man was specifically after me."

"Maybe he wasn't," said Hilts, lifting his shoulder. He ran a finger through the condensation on the outside of his glass. "Maybe he planned to come after you first, and when he was finished with you he'd be waiting for me back at the bike. He'd be rid of both of us, just like whoever hired him to do the job wanted."

"And how do we find out who that was?"

Hilts picked up his glass at last and held it up in a mock toast. "By getting up bright and early tomorrow and flying into enemy territory."

8

She dreamed she saw Baqir dying again and woke up in her room, the light curtains across the balcony doors blowing inward with a soft sound like ghostly wings. She lay alone in the dark listening to the distant sounds of the city and the traffic on the Corniche El Nil far below. How much death and dying had the Nile seen in all the years it had flowed through this place, on its way to Alexandria and the sea?

The curtains whispered again and she sat up a little, pulling the sheet up around her shoulders against the chill. She checked the glowing dial on her watch. Three a.m. She remembered a song her father had played to her mother once, very late one Christmas Eve when she was young, plinking it out on the old stand-up piano in one corner of the living room that nobody ever played. She'd only heard it that one time but the memory was as bright and clear as the love and affection that had prompted her father to sing it:

It's three o'clock in the morning
We've danced the whole night thru,
And daylight soon will be dawning,
Just one more waltz with you.
That melody so entrancing,

Seems to be made for us two,
I could just keep right on dancing
Forever, dear, with you.

A long way from death and the banks of the Nile. Suddenly, lying there, she realized she wasn't alone in the room. A shadow shifted, and as she stared into the far corner the shadow became a shape, and the shape became a man. He cleared his throat and a match flared for a moment, lighting up a round, sweating face wearing glasses. A man in his sixties perhaps, thin hair the yellow white of nicotine. He had fat lips and a small chin. The cigarette he was smoking was oval. She smelled strong, dark tobacco. She had an image of Hilts with the small black pistol in his hand, but Hilts was a couple of floors down. She glanced toward the bedside table. Wallet, keys, the disposable camera she'd never got around to using. Nothing even vaguely resembling a weapon. Not to mention the fact that she slept in the nude. She pushed back against the padded headboard and drew the sheet up a little higher. How the hell had he managed to get in? Like every other hotel in the world these days, the Hilton used electronic key cards.

"I bribed a chambermaid, they all have master keys," said a voice from the darkness, reading her mind. The cigarette glowed and reflected off the man's wire-framed spectacles. "If you stay in Egypt long enough you'll come to realize that everyone in this country can be bribed. Baksheesh of a sort." The man's accent had once been British but had long since become something pale and distant, the lonely voice of the expatriate. "There are several different kinds, you know. There is the baksheesh

48

of the beggar in which the person who offers alms obtains God's grace, then there is the—"

Finn cut him off. "Can you tell me what you're doing in my bedroom, and maybe who you are?"

"I haven't introduced myself, have I? Beg pardon. The name is Simpson, Arthur Simpson. I'd give you my card but I seem to have run out." He took another puff on his evil-smelling cigarette, then crossed his legs and tapped the ash into his trouser cuff. "I'm a guide of sorts. Tours of the Great Pyramid and the Sphinx, interpreting for Germans and Swiss, deciphering hieroglyphics for old dears from Upper Tooting."

Finn stared into the darkness. He sounded like John Cleese doing some sort of bizarre monologue from an old *Monty Python* episode. "You still haven't told me why you're in my hotel room."

Simpson laughed quietly. "Your virtue is un-threatened, Miss Ryan, I can assure you. I'm far too old for that sort of thing."

"That's no answer," said Finn.

"Not an answer." Simpson sighed. "Simply a statement of fact, I'm afraid." He paused and dragged deeply on his cigarette. Finn saw that he was much older than she'd thought originally. His rotundness disguised an unhealthy complexion and dark circles under the eyes. His lips were chapped and dry and there was a sprinkle of day-old gray bristle on his chin. Finally he spoke again. "Actually, Miss Ryan, I'm here to warn you."

"What about?"

Simpson changed the subject again. "I knew your father, you know."

"What are you talking about?"

"We were at Cambridge together."

Finn stared across the room. The fact that her father had gone to Cambridge on a GI Bill fellowship to do post-graduate work wasn't the kind of information one could just pick up anywhere. On the other hand, it wasn't a state secret either. "He never mentioned an Arthur Simpson that I can remember."

"We shared a set for two years."

"Set?"

"Rooms at Magdalene. As in a set of rooms. Dodgy university doublespeak, I'm afraid. You can get degrees in the subject. Semiotics or semantics or some such nonsense."

"Why don't you try getting to the point so you can get out of here."

"Yes, quite. Well, as I said, I knew your father and he knew me, which was much more to the point. You might even say that we became colleagues."

"You were an archaeologist?"

"Good lord, no! I was a spy."

Finn pulled the sheet higher. The fact that her father had worked for the CIA using his role as a research and field archaeologist as a blind was certainly not everyday information. "What does that have to do with my dad?"

"Don't be coy, dear, it doesn't suit you, or serve the memory of your father. You know as well as I do what he was up to in all those jungles he visited."

"Get on with your story," said Finn.

Simpson stubbed out his cigarette in the ashtray and immediately pulled out his crumpled pack and lit another one using a battered old Ronson. He snapped the lighter closed with a hard flat click, then began to talk again.

And Finn listened.

9

The twin-engined Cessna Caravan droned on through the overheated early-afternoon air high above the vast, rippling dunescape of the Libyan Desert. Hilts sat in the pilot's seat, manning the controls and whistling softly under his breath. Beside him was Finn Ryan, her sunglasses protecting her eyes from the almost impossible glare. Behind them were the two other passengers, Achmed the driver, head back against the gray leather seat, eyes closed and mouth open, snoring loudly, and beside him, face buried in a book, the monk, Fr. Jean-Baptiste Laval. He was in his early forties. He wore his graying hair in a buzz cut and had a powerful physique that didn't seem to fit with his chosen way of life. He looked more like a marine than an expert in Coptic inscriptions. The old, leather-bound book in his hands had the title *Vita S. Antoni* along the spine in gold—the Life of Saint Anthony. Behind the two men the cargo bay was packed with the last load of fresh supplies for the dig.

So far the flight from the civil airport in the Giza district had been uneventful. After the brief, breathtaking beauty of the pyramids there had been nothing but broken desert and sand. Now, flying over the Great Sand Sea, the monotony of the dunes seemed as relentless as any empty, windswept ocean. Achmed had fallen asleep almost immediately after takeoff, and Laval the monk had taken out his book a few seconds after undoing his seat belt. He hadn't said a dozen words to anybody and seemed unlikely to in the foreseeable future.

Finn glanced over at Hilts. So far she hadn't said a word to him about her conversation with the mysterious Mr. Simpson the night before. According to the fat little man, at least one of the members of the Adamson expedition was working for the CIA, and Simpson thought there might be more espionage than archaeology involved in the dig. According to him no one could be trusted, least of all Adamson himself. Simpson knew as much about the expedition leader's background as Hilts and more besides.

According to the Cambridge-educated expatriate, Adamson was a secret supporter of the Tenth Crusade, a violent right-wing organization that believed that Christianity was under overt attack and had to be defended with military action. Finn was vaguely aware of the fringe group, which, unlike most of the so-called Patriot Militia, committed their violence well away from the United States. In the last few years the Tenth Crusade, with their cross and roman numeral X insignia, had taken responsibility for attacks in Baghdad, Tehran, Kabul, and Belfast.

The spokesman of the organization was Colonel James Matoon Judd, a Vietnam War Medal of Honor winner, and now the junior senator from Colorado. A fanatic right-wing fundamentalist, Judd was generally thought to be a complete outer-limits nutcase who had been twice warned in the Senate for his racist, inflammatory remarks. The fact that Adamson had anything to do with a lunatic like Senator Jimmy "Sword of the Lord" Judd came as a complete surprise to Finn.

Simpson wasn't entirely sure what Adamson's involvement with Judd had to do with the dig, but according to Simpson it was Judd's influence in the corridors of power that had gotten Adamson's expedition access to the Libyan site. That Judd would be rubbing shoulders with people who were the sworn enemies of groups like the Tenth Crusade didn't make the slightest bit of sense, but according to Simpson's sources it was unqualified fact, and that made the information all the more intriguing.

After Simpson finally left her room, Finn had spent a confusing hour in the darkness trying to make sense of it all, and trying to make the fat little Englishman's tale fit in with what had happened to her in the City of the Dead. What had started off as an exotic summer job after graduation was turning into something sinister, dark, and very dangerous. On top of everything else she still hadn't figured out what Simpson's angle was; except for the tenuous connection to her late father, there was no reason for the strange man to have sought her out for his late-night warning.

"Holy... !"

The Cessna suddenly yawed, turning in the sky like a windblown leaf. They dropped like a stone, surrounded by a screaming howl of jet engines on both sides that came and went in an instant.

"Son of a bitch!" Hilts yelled, struggling with the wheel, hauling back, desperately pulling out of the sudden dive. The horizon tumbled, spun, then finally settled down. "What the hell was that?!"

Finn tried to get her stomach back where it belonged. Achmed, wide awake, sat behind her looking terrified.

Laval, book in his lap, looked out the port-side window, staring through the lightly tinted glass. "I believe they were Sukhoi Su-22s," he said. "A pair of them. Probably flying out of Al-Jufra/Hun. Presumably we are now in Libyan air space. They were most likely trying to read your tail registration number."

"You seem to know a lot about Russian all-purpose fighter jets for a monk," said Hilts. "Not to mention Libyan air bases."

"You forget, Mr. Hilts, I am French, and France had no argument with the colonel, as you Americans had. I have been to this country many times in the past twenty years; I am no stranger to their security measures."

"That must be nice for you," said Hilts with a sour note in his voice.

"It must be disturbing for a man such as yourself to realize that some of us would rather be citizens of the world than citizens of the United States."

Hilts muttered something under his breath.

"I beg your pardon, Mr. Hilts?"

"How soon before we land?" Finn broke in. The thought of these two in a fistfight at twenty thousand feet wasn't doing much for her peace of mind.

"Can't be soon enough for me," Hilts grunted.

10

An hour later they landed at Al-Kufrah. From the air it looked like an arid west Texas ghost town: a crossroads with a main street and a few dozen low, adobe-style buildings in the middle of nowhere. The original oasis had become one of Qaddafi's first "modernization projects" after the revolution, and as they came in for their approach Finn saw dozens of the huge green circles in the desert that marked the deeply irrigated zones of oasis agriculture the colonel-dictator had instituted. The fact that the desert climate was totally unsuited to the crops he tried to grow and that the oasis economy had been totally upset by his efforts was immaterial. He would make the desert bloom even if what he grew cost three times as much to produce as it could be sold for. What Colonel Qaddafi wanted, Colonel Qaddafi got, no questions asked.

Hilts put the Caravan down on the tarmac without so much as a bump and taxied along to the hardstand next to the small terminal building. The airport was an Italian leftover from World War Two and had very little over the years. The run-way had been extended slightly but the square lump of concrete that passed for a terminal was the same, and so was the squat control tower. On the hardstand next to them were two helicopters— one a vicious-looking Mil-24 gunship, squatting like a hunchbacked dragonfly in spotty desert camouflage bristling with weapons, the other a big French-made Aérospatiale Super Puma transport. The Super Puma was white and carried the yellow, black, and red Adamson Corporation Flying A logo on its side.

Three men were standing in front of the Aérospatiale, two in khaki safari-style clothes that looked just a little too stylish to be true, the third man wearing a sky-blue beret and camouflage fatigues that matched the gunship helicopter. He was short, skinny, and had a face like a long-nosed ferret, complete with bushy eyebrows and a cop's mustache over thin lips. His eyes were hidden behind mirrored aviator sunglasses.

"With sunglasses like that he's got to be one of the bad guys," said Hilts. He popped open the pilot's door of the Cessna, letting in a blast of dry, hot air that hit him like a fist after the interior air conditioning. He stepped out, dropping down onto the hardstand. Finn opened her own door and followed him out. Achmed and the monk roused themselves and came out through the rear door. One of the men in the khaki shooting jackets waved. Finn recognized him from the *Newsweek* profile. It was Rolf Adamson, the forty-year-old media tycoon, billionaire, possible religious fanatic, and also her new boss. He looked exactly like his photograph in the magazine: young, blond, Hollywood handsome and New York smart. The man beside him was the direct opposite, old, grizzled, and dark with the face of a worn-out prizefighter.

"The one in the *Lion King* outfit beside our fearless leader Mr. Adamson is Fritz Kuhn," said Hilts quietly. "His grandfather was a man named Gustav Kossina, sometimes referred to as Hitler's archaeologist. Kossina was the freak who came up with all those 'scientific' theories about Aryan supremacy."

"What's he doing here?"

"He's written a bunch of books about the Italian digs around Al-Kufrah before the war and about Pedrazzi, the guy who disappeared." He held up two fingers twined together. "Kossina and Pedrazzi were buddies in the old days. Adamson's hired Kuhn as a consultant." He glanced at the ferret-faced man in the beret. "Presumably Mr. Gung Ho is our military escort."

They made their way over to the three men, with Laval bringing up the rear. Achmed started unloading the Cessna. Everyone made their introductions. The man in uniform turned out to be Lieutenant Colonel Amad Nasif, Colonel Qaddafi's personal guide and "protector" of the expedition. There was no explanation of what the man in the beret would be protecting the expedition from.

"The Guide of the First of September Great Revolution of the Arab Libyan Popular and Socialist Jamahirya is particularly concerned that nothing happen to our new American guests," said Nasif with a little bow. Finn had never heard Qaddafi's title in full before, and out of the corner of her eye she could see Hilts trying not to laugh. It was clear that Nasif took the title seriously. His expression looked as though it was carved out of granite.

Adamson clapped his hands together with a grin. "I don't think we have to worry about that, Colonel. I think we've got everything under control." Adamson had a deep, rich voice and a vaguely Kennedyesque accent, even though he had been born and raised on the West Coast. His smile showed off a set of expensive teeth. Everybody watched as Achmed and two men from Nasif's helicopter loaded up the Super Puma.

"My people tell me you can fly one of these," said Adamson to Hilts, nodding at the French chopper.

"I can fly anything," the pilot answered, smiling and looking pointedly across the hardstand to Nasif's sinister-looking Mil-24.

"Show me," said Adamson. "The charts are in the door pocket. I'll fly the copilot's seat."

"You're rated on this?" Hilts said, surprised.

Adamson smiled. "If it's got my name on it, I'm rated for it." The two men stared at each other briefly. Finn felt as though she was in the middle of a pissing contest and it surprised her. She didn't think Hilts was the type, and Adamson should have been too rich to care.

Boys will be boys, she thought with a sigh. She pulled open the big sliding door, climbed up the single welded step, and ducked into the lavishly appointed passenger cabin of the transport helicopter. A few minutes later, following Nasif in the gunship, they rose heavily off the hardstand and took to the air once more.

11

From the air the site at Deir el-Shakir looked more like a science-fiction moon base than an archaeological dig. Two dozen huge, white nylon high-tech yurts, or domed tents, were scattered across a plateau above a narrow sandstone valley that marked the ancient bed of a long-vanished river. The yurts, each with a forty-foot diameter, were connected by arched nylon tunnels. There were several more lozenge-shaped arch-roof tents that served as living quarters, offices, and even as garages and maintenance sheds for the expedition's fleet of Range Rovers and Hummer Alphas. The domes and tunnels all had a single purpose: to protect the occupants—man or machine—from the constant winds and the eroding, choking, ever-present dust and sand. The two largest structures, anchored, guy-wired, and lag-bolted into sunken concrete columns, were the two hangars used to house Adamson's transport chopper and the single-engine Polish PZL "Wilga" that Hilts would be using as his aerial photography platform. With a takeoff requiring only five hundred feet of run-way, the PZL was just about the only aircraft available that could fly in and out of the site. Between the two hangars was a GFI portable helipad to smooth out the rough, pitted area of rock and sand and to keep down flying debris.

Hilts put the big transport down without a quaver, then switched off. As soon as the rotors slowed, four men in white uniforms like cruise ship stewards appeared, and without waiting for the passengers to climb down they rolled the helicopter into the big hangar tent and pulled the Velcro closers on the hangar doors. Like the helipad outside, the floor of the hangar was covered in heavy-duty composite mats to create a stable, clean area. The passenger compartment door slid open and Finn and the others climbed out. Achmed and the men who'd rolled the helicopter inside began unloading.

"Well, Ms. Ryan, what do you think?" Adamson asked, smiling proudly.

Finn wasn't quite sure what to say, or why she was being singled out by the expedition leader for attention. "Impressive," she answered.

"Expensive," added Hilts.

"Very," Adamson said and nodded. "At last count it was several million dollars."

"I'm not sure the Copts would approve," said Hilts. "If I remember right, they took a vow of poverty."

"True enough," put in Laval. "On the other hand, most of the hermetic Copts, such as the ones who lived Deir el-Shakir, were fleeing debts."

"People have always run into the desert in the hopes of disappearing." Adamson laughed. "That's what the French Foreign Legion was designed for." They walked across the hangar and went into one of the connecting tunnels. The steady wind outside whispered against the heavy nylon, rippling the fabric slightly and making a faint slapping sound.

61

"Almasy," said Finn. It was just about the only concrete thing she knew about this part of the world.

"I beg your pardon," said Adamson, stopping to turn and stare at her. The blood seemed to drain from his face. For the first time Finn knew what people meant when they said someone went white as a sheet.

"Almasy," she repeated. "The Hungarian count from *The English Patient*."

"*The English Patient* was a novel," snapped Adamson.

"Pretty good movie too," put in Hilts. "Willem Dafoe was really terrific. Not as good as he was in *Spider-Man*, but still terrific."

Adamson glared at him.

"Almasy was based on a real person though, wasn't he?" insisted Finn, surprised and more than a little curious at Adamson's reaction.

Laval shook his head. He gave Finn another one of his small, patronizing smiles. A little girl being patted on the head. "Laszlo Almasy wasn't a count at all. His father was a high-level government official in Budapest. A *fonctionaire*, as it were, that's all. The way Germans are all *herr doctor* or *herr professor*. He fled to the desert because he'd had an affair with a politician's wife. He was paid to stay there. He was a dilettante, Ms. Ryan, nothing more."

"I thought he was a spy during World War Two," said Hilts flatly. "He used what he knew about the desert to bring a spy across from Morocco all the way to Cairo, right?"

"There are many stories about Laszlo Almasy," said Laval with a faint smile, "and most of them are just that, stories."

"And none of them have anything at all to do with Coptic monasteries in general or Deir el-Shakir in particular," said Adamson. He made an imperious little motion with his hand. "Come along."

They followed Adamson along the gently curving passageway, finally exiting into a large living area complete with tables, chairs, a portable kitchen with a refrigerator, and both a Ping-Pong and a billiard table. There were several people in the large, domed room, some reading or talking together. An Asian man and a black woman were playing a spirited game of Ping-Pong. Everyone was dressed casually. The atmosphere in the dome was cool, and Finn suddenly realized that it was air conditioned. Light came in through half a dozen translucent triangles set into the walls. Somewhere nearby she could hear the faint hum of a generator.

Adamson guided them to one of the tables and they sat down. A few moments later another uniformed steward appeared with a tray loaded down with a jug of iced tea, sprigs of mint, and glasses that looked as though they'd been stored in a freezer. The steward was dark-haired and olive-skinned. His name tag read "Badir." A local like the ones in the helicopter hangar. The steward withdrew silently. Playing the host, Adamson poured iced tea for everyone and sat back in his chair.

"There are ninety-two people on site at Deir el-Shakir," he said. "Of those, twenty-five are actually on the archaeological staff, fifteen are interning graduate students from universities around the world, twenty more are volunteers who pay for the privilege of being here, and the rest are support staff. This is one of the most sophisticated and expensive archaeological sites on the planet. In addition to the services of Mr. Hilts, we have a complete remote-sensing department, which includes hookups to SPOT, French Satellite Pour l'Observation de la Terre archives, NASA Landsat, and ASTER. We also have full side-scanning radar facilities, computer imaging, and real-time access to some of the world's most comprehensive archaeological archives. In short, if you want information, we can get it for you."

"Good to know," said Hilts, looking around at the dome.

"You will be running a number of low-altitude surveys using both film and digital cameras. We have the plots and charts any time you'd like to see them," offered Adamson.

"Satellites don't give you enough?"

"A great deal of data, but not much detail. We're particularly interested in the location of old caravan trails and the wells that were used by pilgrims coming to the monastery."

"Seems straightforward."

"Hopefully." Adamson turned to Finn. "You, Ms. Ryan, will be spending most of your time doing in situ drawings of artifacts before their removal, then placing those locations on the overall site grid. I understand from your résumé that you have some experience with computers."

"Some."

"PitCalc? Altview?"

"Yes." PitCalc was one of the earliest pieces of archaeology software written and one that she'd learned on her mother's computer in the field when she was a teenager. Altview was the same kind of wire-diagram program draftsmen used. It was one of those times when she was glad she hadn't fluffed her résumé like a lot of her friends, some to the point of adding entire degrees or past job descriptions.

"Good," said Adamson. He drained his iced tea and stood. "Achmed will have taken your luggage to your quarters. As staff members you both have private quarters in the residential quadrant." A white-coated steward silently appeared at the table. Adamson laid a paternal hand on the young man's shoulder. "Farag will show you the way." Finn was surprised that Adamson knew who the steward was until she noticed the plastic name tag pinned to his jacket. "Until dinner this evening," Adamson said and smiled. Then he turned on his heel and left. They watched him go.

"I wonder what Deir el-Shakir means," said Finn, taking a sip of her iced tea.

"Monastery of the Skull," supplied Hilts. "The skull in question was supposed to have belonged to St. Thomas the Apostle. That's what the Copts meditated on here. There's also a theory that the skull was made of crystal, like that Mayan one, except the skull here was supposedly that of Baphomet... the Knights Templar version of Satan. Spooky if you're a fan of that kind of thing."

Finn laughed. "You've been watching *X-Files* reruns, haven't you?"

"If you'll follow me, please," murmured Farag, their steward.

And they did.

12

True to Adamson's word, Finn's luggage had been delivered to her quarters in the residence quadrant, a long domed yurt like the others but with individual rooms jutting out from the main tent like the legs of a centipede. By her count there were twenty-five of these cells, each one equipped with electricity, a gravity-fed water tank, and a small chemical toilet cubicle. The quarters also had a smaller version of the triangular windows in the recreational area. She had a camp bed with an inflatable mattress and matching pillow, a tubular steel and plastic desk, a lamp, a Local Area Network Internet connection for a laptop, and a chair. She even had her very own air-conditioning duct. For communications there was a headset Motorola ten-channel walkie-talkie outfit with a five-mile range and a buzzer system for calling a steward if necessary. Everything she needed to know about the site from a plan of the "moon base" to instructions for flushing the chemical toilet was contained in a loose-leaf binder lying on her bed. Adamson had clearly spared no expense, and Finn found herself wondering what he was hoping to get for all his money. It seemed like overkill for a few Coptic inscriptions, since according to Hilts the monastery was far from a newly discovered site.

The evening meal was held in the dining hall, a large yurt like the recreation area with two dozen tables, including a large one for the actual staff in an area separated from the rest of the tables by a high, white nylon barrier. Finn found herself seated between a ceramic expert from the Royal Ontario Museum named Adrian March and Hilts. Adamson sat at the head of the table beside a small dark man he introduced as Mustapha Hisnawi, their liaison with the Libyan Office of Antiquities. Directly across from her was Fritz Kuhn, the heavyset man Hilts had said was the grandson of Hitler's archaeologist. Beside him was Laval, the monk from l'Ecole Biblique in Jerusalem. The meal was a variety of Libyan dishes, lamb, chicken, and vegetarian. The conversation was mostly about the dig and mostly technical. Finn waited for an opportune moment and finally managed to ask her question.

"Is there any real focus to the dig?" she said. Across from her the German, Kuhn, frowned. Adamson just shrugged.

"Does there have to be a focus?"

"Usually for a project like this you'd expect some sort of ultimate goal."

"What would you know about projects like this," Kuhn snorted, digging around at the sauce-covered lamb and rice on his plate. His face was flushed. He picked up his wineglass and drained it. A steward appeared at his back and refilled it from a cloth-swathed bottle. Finn ignored Kuhn's rudeness and waited for Adamson's answer.

"Archaeology is a science of small increments, Ms. Ryan. The man seated beside you, young Dr. March, will spend several years collecting enough pieces from a shattered pot to make a reconstruction, and even then it will probably not be complete. But completeness is not the goal, is it, Adrian?"

"Dear me, no," said the slim, fair-haired man with the thick glasses who sat on her left. "One looks for trends, points of comparison. Complete reconstructions aren't necessary to know what one is dealing with."

"There you are, Ms. Ryan. Our overall goal here at Deir el-Shakir is simply to add to the sum total of what we already know. This is not Howard Carter uncovering King Tut's tomb, or a French captain of engineers discovering the Rosetta Stone as he prepared to blow up a bridge. Nothing that would be worthy of the *CBS Evening News,* believe me, not even Larry King." He laughed. "This is simply the basic gathering of knowledge so that we have a better picture about the past."

"Trudging in the fields of academe, tilling the soil of history, that kind of thing?" Hilts quipped. He picked up a chicken bone on his plate and sucked off a remaining piece of meat. He dropped the bone back on the plate, then wiped his hands on a napkin.

"Something like that, Virgil," Adamson said with a nod.

"Just Hilts, if you don't mind. Just Hilts."

"As I understand it, Deir el-Shakir was originally founded by St. Thomas the Apostle," said Finn, remembering what Hilts had told her.

"A myth," Laval answered from the opposite side of the table. "Historically St. Thomas is presumed to have gone in the opposite direction, to India. Deir el-Shakir was born out of what is usually referred to as the Arian heresy, Arius being a well-known monk from Libya. He preached that Christ was not divine, but mortal, and merely a prophet; it is probably this doubt about Christ being the true Son of God that suggested the link to Thomas, a man given to the same sort of thinking, ergo the nickname 'Doubting Thomas.' The monks here were followers of Arius, but I'm afraid St. Thomas was not among them."

"And the skull?" Finn asked. She turned to Adamson, trying to gauge his reaction.

"What skull would that be?"

"I think it's called the Skull of Baphomet," said Finn.

Adamson burst out laughing. Laval smiled broadly. "I'm afraid you're getting your Knights Templar fantasies mixed up," Adamson said, grinning. "Just because a book is on the *New York Times* Bestseller List doesn't mean it's true, especially if it's on the fiction side. What you're talking about is the supposed flight of Nicodemus and Joseph of Arimathea to England. The head on the shield of the Templar Grand Master was a representation of the skull of one of the earlier French knights named Hughes de Payen... who lived about seven hundred years after the monks here were already dust."

"You know a lot about the Templars," said Hilts quietly.

"I know a lot about a lot of things," answered Adamson. Dinner went on for a little while longer and then people began excusing themselves. As Hilts stood to go he whispered in Finn's ear.

"He's lying. There's something else going on."

Finn didn't answer. She looked down the table at Adamson, who was lost in conversation with the Libyan liaison officer, Hisnawi. Suddenly the expedition leader turned and stared down the table at her. The glance was utterly cold and without emotion. She held his hawklike gaze for a second longer, and he finally looked away. Finn stood up and shivered. If looks could kill she'd be a corpse. The expression had been exactly the same as the one on the killer's face in the City of the Dead.

13

"I've been here for two weeks and there's been nothing out of the ordinary," said Finn. She and Hilts were in the dining room on a coffee break. For the past two weeks they'd barely exchanged a dozen words. Hilts had flown a seemingly endless series of flights charting a low-altitude grid around the dig site and Finn had made exact drawings of a seemingly endless series of pottery shards. "Maybe Adamson really is operating on the up-and-up."

Hilts pulled a face. "I don't have to remind you about what happened in Cairo."

"Which might have had more to do with you than me."

Hilts sighed. "You don't really believe that, do you?"

"If Adamson was out to kill me, why would he have wanted me on the expedition staff in the first place?"

"Keep your friends close but your enemies closer, as the Godfather once said."

Finn laughed. "I think the quote is actually Sun Tzu from *The Art of War,* but I get your point... only how did I get to be Adamson's enemy?"

Hilts played with the lip of his coffee cup. "I've spent a fair bit of time thinking about that. The only thing I could think of was Mickey Hearts."

"I wish you wouldn't call him that."

"Sorry... Mr. Valentine. Anyway, he's the only thing that makes sense, the only connection."

"How do you figure?"

"He got you the job, didn't he?"

"I like to think my qualifications had something to do with it."

"No offense, sweetheart, but there's a lot of technical illustrators out there with a lot more experience than you. And how did you hear about the job in the first place?"

"My faculty advisor told me about it."

"How did he know about it?"

"He said he had a friend who told him about it."

"Check it out. I bet you'll find out that the friend in question was Mickey... your Mr. Valentine."

"Why would Michael put my life in jeopardy?"

"Did he say anything to you before you left New York?"

"I put him down as a reference for the job. I called to make sure it was okay."

"What did he say?"

"He said fine. He seemed to know about the job already."

"And?"

"He told me to be careful."

"A warning?"

"I didn't think so at the time. I thought he was talking about foreign travel, watching out for pickpockets, that kind of thing."

"And now?" Hilts asked.

Finn paused, thinking. Hilts started tearing little chunks out of the top of his foam cup. "Now I guess I'm not so sure anymore. It could have been a warning, but that still doesn't answer my question. Why would he knowingly send me into danger? That is, if he got me the job in the first place, which is what you seem to think."

"I wondered about that too. I think maybe your friend thought he was doing you a favor at first, but something changed his mind."

"Like what?"

"Like he found out something."

"Found out something like what?"

"Like this," said Hilts, keeping his voice low. He reached into the pocket of his worn and faded fatigue jacket and brought out a device only a little larger than a cell phone.

Finn looked at the tiny piece of electronics. "What is it?"

"A Garmin i-Que."

"I'm not too good at the hi-tech stuff," said Finn. "Words that an art history major can understand."

"It's a GPS recorder, as in Global Positioning System."

"I don't get it."

"Have you been keeping track of our esteemed leader?"

"Qaddafi? No, I'm not in the dictator's loop."

"Ha-ha. Adamson. Particularly Adamson and his pals Kuhn and Hisnawi, our man from Museums and Antiquities."

"I've been far too busy drawing little pictures of broken pieces of thousand-year-old clay pots, which are of no interest whatsoever."

"I'm busy flying patterns with the Polish answer to powered flight most days, which is probably just about as boring as sketching old chamber pots, but it does have one advantage."

"Which is?"

"I'm at twelve thousand feet. I get to see a lot. Mostly sand."

"Get to the point."

"Every day for the last week or so Adamson, Kuhn, and Hisnawi take out one of those desert Hummers and head out into the desert."

"How do you know it's them?" asked Finn.

Hilts reached into his pocket again and took out a crumpled piece of photo paper. "As well as regular film cameras, Adamson uses a Belgian thing called a DIMAC... Digital Modular Aerial Camera. Like most aerial cameras it's set to take slightly oblique images... from the side, to give shadow and scale." He smoothed out the picture on the table. It was fuzzy, but the faces were clear. "It's Adamson, Hisnawi, and the German, no doubt about it. I downloaded the shot onto my laptop, enhanced it and blew it up." Finn looked at the picture. All three were visible, Adamson behind the wheel, Hisnawi on the seat beside him, and Kuhn seated in the back. Something was in the truck bed, covered with a tarp.

Finn shrugged. "So what? Hisnawi, Kuhn, and Adamson go for rides in the desert, what's the big deal?"

Hilts prodded the little GPS device. "I managed to slip this behind the spare tire of Adamson's personal Hummer, the yellow and black one that looks like a giant bumblebee? They go to the exact same coordinates every time."

"Where?"

"One hundred and eight miles almost due west of here." He punched a button on the device to retrieve the numbers. "North twenty-one degrees, fifty-two minutes, and thirty seconds by east twenty-three degrees, thirty-two minutes, eighteen seconds, to be absolutely precise."

"What's there?"

"Absolutely nothing."

"Be logical, Hilts, there has to be something there or they wouldn't be going."

"According to the charts it's at the edge of a small plateau. If the sky were red you could be on Mars. Rocks and sand."

Finn sighed. "Mars has an atmosphere. The sky is actually blue."

"Sorry, Dr. Ryan."

"I had to take a couple of straight science courses. One of them was astrophysics."

"The point is, there really is nothing there. I even checked to see if it was on one of the old caravan routes. Nada. Just more rocks and sand until you get to the Algerian border."

"What happens then?"

"You get Algerian rocks and sand instead of Libyan rocks and sand."

"You really are a pain, you know that, don't you?"

"It's a gift."

"What do you *think* is out there, Hilts?"

"I think they found what they were actually looking for."

"Which is?"

"Only one way to find out."

14

They flew over the endless desert, heading west, seeing nothing. The cockpit of the little high-winged aircraft was cramped and the rear two seats had been replaced with a variety of bulky camera equipment and a long-range fuel tank to give the pilot the extra in-flight hours needed to fly large-scale grid series.

Finn stared out through the large side window. "You were right," she said. "Absolutely nothing. More rocks than sand, I'd say."

"It's more hamada than erg."

"Easy for you to say," Finn said and laughed.

"Hamada is a rocky desert, an erg is one made up of dunes. Out here the hamada usually is a function of altitude. The higher the elevation the stonier the ground. Mind you, it hasn't always been this way."

"It looks like it's been this way since time began."

"Probably less than four or five thousand years. You mentioned the *English Patient* a while back... remember the Cave of Swimmers?"

"The cave that Almasy found."

"It's real. And they really are swimming. The actual cave is at a place called Wadi Sora in Egypt. Five thousand years ago there was no desert here, just hills and plateaus

76

and rivers and lots of animals. Think about all those lion safari movies you've seen and you'll have it right."

"Hard to believe."

"That's what they used to say about global warming too. Take it back far enough and you'll find that all that sand started out on the Atlantic beaches in Morocco. When we get back from our little spy mission I'll show you some infrared satellite images that'll knock your socks off. You can still see the markers where the old rivers used to flow, enormous ones that used to irrigate the whole of northern Africa."

"Maybe that has something to do with what Adamson and his pals are after, some kind of site like the Cave of Swimmers?"

"Zerzura, that old fantasy? I doubt it very much. He has aspirations as an archaeologist, not as a paleontologist, and I don't think Brother Laval, our cheerful monk from Jerusalem, cares much about cave art." Hilts shook his head. "No, I think it might be something from the war."

"Which one."

"World War Two. It would explain Kuhn's involvement."

"But why?"

"This whole area was crawling with Germans, Brits, and Italians during the early part of the war. There was also a lot of Italian activity even before that. Pedrazzi, the Italian I told you about, was a well-known archaeologist, but he could have been a spy too. Just about everybody was back then."

"Things don't seem to have changed much," said Finn dryly.

"We're not really spying, we're just satisfying our curiosity."

"That's what got the cat in trouble, as I recall."

On the horizon a darker line began to grow, slowly resolving itself into a rough, lifeless plateau of rock, cracked and broken into a thousand narrow valleys and trackless canyons leading nowhere. Hilts had used a smart cable to plug the cell-phone-sized GPS locater into the larger version on the airplane's instrument panel. As they approached the plateau he scanned the color display, watching the readout and adjusting the plane's small, doughnut-shaped control wheel, making small adjustments to bring them to the exact coordinates.

"Almost there," he muttered, veering slightly to the right. "See anything?"

"Not yet."

"I'm going to take it down." Hilts dropped the nose and the small plane responded almost instantly, gliding downward so smoothly it seemed to Finn that they were sliding along some invisible wire. Whatever else Hilts was, he certainly knew how to fly, she thought. She stared out through the side window and then she saw it, almost directly under them.

"There!"

"What?"

"Tracks. I can see tire tracks."

Hilts tilted the plane into a slow turn, staring out his own side window. After a moment he spotted the same broad tracks below them. "Follow the trail of breadcrumbs," he said and took the plane down again, flying along above the tire tracks at less than a thousand feet now. The twin lines were almost perfectly straight, heading directly for a narrow canyon entrance visible in the distance.

"Where do we land?"

"Just about anywhere. My girl here is the ultimate in short takeoff and landing. The landing gear has underinflated tires and we only need five hundred feet or so to take off in. I'll take us in as close as possible."

"How accurate is that GPS thing?"

"Spitting distance. Plus or minus ten, fifteen yards in any direction."

Finn watched as Hilts concentrated on his flying, his fingers on the control stick as light as a lover's. His eyes flickered between the rapidly approaching surface of the stony desert and his instruments. It was almost like watching an impresario playing the violin. He started whistling under his breath and Finn recognized the tune; it was the theme music for *The Flintstones*. She smiled, watching as he made a few final adjustments, compensating for a tugging wind that shuddered through the airplane briefly as they sank to the ground. The wheels touched with a barely noticeable thump and then they were down, tail wheel first, the sturdy mains a moment later.

15

The plane rolled on, slowing quickly as Hilts backed off on the throttle and dropped his flaps. He turned the plane into the wind and brought it to a full stop, letting the engine run for a full two minutes before switching off. The propeller whirled to a stop and then there was nothing but the sound of the wind brushing against the fuselage and lightly rocking the wings. Directly in front of them, half a football field away, was a high cliff face, cracked and broken, the notch of a canyon prominently etched in shadows just to their left.

"You'd never know there was anything there," said Hilts.

"Maybe there isn't anything," Finn cautioned.

"Right," Hilts said, "they come out here every day with their yoga mats for a bit of meditation and a few updogs."

"You really are a very cynical man, Mr. Hilts."

"Cynical is a fool's word for a realist." Hilts unlatched the top-hinged, large-windowed door and pushed it up toward the wing. He ducked through the opening and stepped out into the blistering sun. Finn did the same on her side, then walked around and joined Hilts.

"How long do you think we have?"

"They never leave before two in the afternoon, and we're at least an hour away by Hummer. So we've got at least an hour and a half before we should be gone."

"It would help if we knew what we were looking for."

"The Hummer tracks lead right into that canyon."

"What about our tracks? Will they see them?"

"The plane weighs less than a ton. The Hummer weighs four times that much." He pointed. "Look at the ruts; they've broken through the surface crust and left a trail you could probably see from the space shuttle. Not the most environmentally friendly vehicle in the world, and you can see they've been out here half a dozen times. Our track is barely noticeable."

"Cynical and very sure of yourself."

"Quit worrying; they'll never know we were here." He went back under the wing, ducked into the plane and came out again with one of the old Nikons he'd had with him in the City of the Dead and a couple of canteens. "Just in case we do find something," he explained, rejoining her. He handed one of the canteens to Finn and she slung it across her shoulder. Together they headed down the deep ruts that marked the recent trail of Adamson and his companions into the desert canyon.

"It's more than just the Hummer," said Finn, staring down at the hard-packed, rock-strewn grit. "There's other tracks here, faint ones."

"Deserts aren't quite the empty places you imagine," said Hilts in reply. "Even before the war this whole area was like Grand Central Station. Brits, French, archaeologists, petroleum geologists. The Italians were here even before that... Graziani laying down hundreds of miles of barbed wire to catch the Senussi rebels, Bagnold exploring, and then with the LRDG."

"LRDG?"

"Long Range Desert Group, aka the Desert Rats. Small commando forces sent out into the desert to harass the Germans and the Italians."

"I thought that kind of thing only went on in the north."

Hilts bent down and used his fingers to dig at a small lump of rock. It turned out to be the bottom edge of a small tin. He tugged it up out of the dirt. There was still part of a blue-and-white printed label visible, with a twist of metal and a key-style attached. He handed the tin to Finn.

"Swift's Plate Corned Beef," she read.

"Some time before Adamson got here the Brits came through. Either military or even before."

"Why here specifically?"

"We're close to three borders, Sudan, Egypt, and what used to be called French Equatorial Africa. Back then there was some strategic importance to a place like this, especially if there was water close by. A wadi in one of the bigger canyons maybe." He shook his head. "Strange how things change over time. It's like Normandy: just a bunch of beaches on the coast of France now, but sixty years ago the fate of the world was focused there."

"Nothing's focused here by the looks of it," said Finn.

"Never can tell," Hilts replied.

They kept moving forward until finally they reached the entrance to the canyon. The opening was barely fifty feet across, one side jutting out a little more than the other so that in anything less than full sunlight shadows would make the opening virtually invisible. Finn and Hilts continued onward into the canyon itself, the rock cliffs rising claustrophobically on either side, narrowing so that the tracks of the Hummer came within a foot or two of the enclosure.

"They weren't first in," said Hilts, nodding toward a number of other, fainter tracks. "Someone knew about this place a long time ago."

A hundred feet along, the canyon suddenly took a sharp turn to the right, straightened, and then became narrower still. Looking at the sandstone walls, Finn could see definite gouges where the heavy bumpers of a truck had dug into the rock. As quickly as it straightened the canyon curved again, this time to the left. A hundred yards farther on the narrow gauntlet broadened into a small, high-sided valley. Hilts and Finn stopped in their tracks, staring into a frozen moment from events that had happened long before they were born.

"My God, what happened here?" Finn whispered, lifting a hand to shade her eyes. The valley floor before them was a tableau of horror. Hilts lifted his Nikon, popped the lens cap and began shooting.

Directly in front of where they stood was the carcass of some sort of military vehicle, an open truck riding on what must have been enormous tires if the size of the rims and the huge curving fenders were any indication. The tires themselves had disappeared, whatever was left of the rubber having disintegrated long ago. The vehicle had been crewed by three men, a driver, a machine gunner beside him, and a man operating a heavy-barreled antitank gun in the rear. The remains of those three men were still in the truck. The mummified body of the driver was thrown back in his seat, his skull grinning, still covered with a parchment of skin and a few ragged strings of scalp. The eye sockets were filled with caked grime and grit from more than half a century of sandstorms and exposure. The machine gunner was a crumpled sack of bones on the cracked leather seat beside the driver, held together by nothing more than the tattered remnants of his uniform. An old ball-shaped helmet sat askew on a headless spine. The third member of the crew might have lived a little longer than his companions; what was left of his body was crouched against the tailgate of the vehicle, head ducked down, the leathery sticks of his arms still wrapped around the empty shell of his desiccated rib cage, as though trying to fend off the chill of death throughout eternity.

Hilts stepped forward and ran his hand over the flank of the vehicle. There were dozens of bullet holes puckering the metal, the holes just big enough to poke his pinkie finger into. Forty-five caliber or less. A light machine gun. The truck was riddled like a tin can used for target practice.

"Italian," the photographer said, stooping to inspect a faded unit designation on the rear of the vehicle. "One hundred and third Compagnie Arditi Camionettisti, a jeep scouting company. They called these trucks *Sahariane*. It was pretty much the first vehicle specially designed for the desert." He stood up.

"Who shot them?" Finn queried.

"They did," answered Hilts, pointing. A hundred yards farther down the valley was a second tableau, this one made up of two trucks, a smaller jeep-like vehicle, and a rough camp spread out on the valley floor, complete with the skeletal remains of several small tents laid out in a half circle around a built-up fire pit, a row of abandoned jerry cans, and a long slit trench. The jeep looked as though it had suffered a direct hit from the big antitank gun on the Italian vehicle. It was blasted and charred, the windshield disintegrated, the wheel rims sunk into the ground. The other two larger trucks were in better shape, their tires vanished but the camouflage markings still visible.

Reaching the vehicles and the ghostly remains of the campsite, Hilts began taking more photographs, concentrating on the work unit markings on the trucks and the old equipment scattered around the camp.

"Red and black stripes with a white scorpion. Guards unit, LRDG. The truck is a thirty hundred-weight British Chevy."

"How do you know all this stuff?"

"I built a lot of models when I was a kid. There was even a TV series about these guys called the Rat Patrol I watched in reruns. It starred Christopher George, if you remember him. Kind of like a cut-rate George Peppard."

"No."

"So much for his career."

"There's no bodies," said Finn, looking around the campsite. "There should be bodies."

Hilts turned and looked back at the Italian truck. He saw immediately that the bullets that had killed the three-man crew probably hadn't come from the direction of the camp. In the first place, the trucks and the burnt-out jeep were placed wrongly, and in the second place, the machine guns on the British vehicles were too heavy: big Vickerses and Brownings as well as an even larger Boys Anti-tank gun mounted on the rear of the second truck. Hilts looked up at the surrounding ragged walls of the steep little valley and then he knew.

"It was an ambush," he said finally, kicking one of the old stamped tin Shell Benzene brand fuel containers with the toe of his boot. "They heard the Italians coming so they went up into the rocks and waited for them. That's why they never got any farther into the valley. Picked them off from above."

Finn walked through the camp, stooping every now and again to examine a rusted piece of equipment or some other faded artifact. "Two trucks and that jeep thing. How many men would that be?"

"Hard to say, as many as a dozen, but since there's only three tents it was probably more like six—two men to each. Shorthanded. Maybe they'd lost a few."

"Six against three and they didn't win?"

"Who said they lost?"

"The trucks are still here. Why didn't they leave? No fuel, no water maybe?"

Hilts shook his head. "These were pretty smart people. They had fuel dumps everywhere and they always left themselves enough gas to get to one, or back to base, whichever was nearer. And all the trucks had condensers for their radiators. Water wouldn't have been a problem."

"Something happened, that's for sure." Finn did a slow, three-hundred-and-eighty-degree turn. "It's an interesting little mystery, but surely this isn't what Adamson was after?"

"I doubt it," agreed Hilts.

"We should keep looking," said Finn. "And we should keep an eye on the time." She looked at her watch. They'd been on the ground for almost half an hour.

Hilts looked into the remains of the tents and then climbed up on the trucks. He jumped down from the bed of the second vehicle and joined Finn, who was looking into the narrow, shallow trench that stood behind the blockading row of sandbags that faced the canyon entrance to the valley.

"Find anything?"

"Tin cans—more corned beef—condensed milk, looks like a weird Birkenstock, a stove made out of a ten-gallon drum with holes punched in it, and this." She handed up the remains of what had once been a black beret. There was a tarnished, sand-scarred badge clipped on the front.

"A scorpion in a circle." He nodded. *"Non Vi Sed Arte*—Not by Strength, by Guile. It's an LRDG cap badge and beret." Hilts reached out and helped her up out of the pit.

"What would have made the Italians come into the canyon in the first place? How would they have found it?" Finn asked as they made their way through the camp and continued to explore.

"Same way we did, I guess," said Hilts. "They followed the tracks of the LRDG trucks."

"Okay, then why did the Brits come in?"

"Looking for a place to camp?"

"Or maybe they were following someone else's tracks as well."

"We'll never know," said Hilts. He stopped. Halfway up the right-hand wall of the valley they saw the wreckage of an airplane. "What the hell … ?"

The old biplane looked as though it had tried to land, lost control on approach, and ran up the side of the valley before it stopped. The engine cowling had ruptured, shattering the propeller, and the lower wing had crumpled and torn, leaving half the upper wing and a few struts. The undercarriage had completely vanished. Over time the desert had taken its toll and the fabric covering on the fuselage was in tatters. What was left showed no signs of national identification.

"Maybe that's what the Brits were after," said Finn, staring at the ruined aircraft. The door of the plane was sagging open and she could see up into the cockpit. The windscreen was cracked but unbroken.

"Maybe that's what Adamson was after too," said Hilts. He climbed up toward the wreckage, pulling himself steadily up the steep slope with his hands digging into the stony sandstone.

"Why would Adamson be interested in an old airplane?"

"Because Lucio Pedrazzi was a flyer. He was one of the first archaeologists to use aerial surveys, and he flew an airplane just like this, a Waco UIC."

"That sounds American."

"It was," Hilts answered. "William Randolph Hearst used to fly one. The *Citizen Kane* guy. It was popular all over the world." They finally reached the wreck, and hanging on to one of the wing struts, Hilts peered into the cockpit. Finn followed suit. There were two bucket seats, the leather rotted, leaving only the springs, a Y-shaped yoke and two Bakelite wheels, one for the pilot, the other for the copilot beside him. The rear section had been enlarged and turned into a cargo bay. It was empty except for an odd skeletal cube formed out of welded aluminum. In the center of the boxlike arrangement was something that looked like a simplified version of a child's gyroscope.

At the base of the cube was a metal sleeve that led down into the fuselage.

"A camera mount?" asked Finn.

Hilts nodded. "A Bagley, or maybe a K-5. But no camera."

"Adamson."

"Could be."

"I thought Pedrazzi was looking for our Coptic monastery."

"Maybe he was looking for something else as well."

"When exactly did Pedrazzi disappear?" asked Finn, staring into the empty cockpit.

"In 1938."

"In a sandstorm?"

Hilts nodded. "That's the story."

"Was he alone?"

"Actually, no. There was a Frenchman with him, as a matter of fact. A man named Pierre DeVaux."

"Who was he?"

An archaeologist. A monk, just like Laval. He was there to help Pedrazzi translate Aramaic inscriptions."

"From l'École Biblique? The Jerusalem School?"

"I'm not sure," said Hilts. "Probably."

Finn found herself thinking about Arthur Simpson, the man in her hotel room. The man who knew her archaeologist father. The man who'd been a British spy. The man whose own father had been an archaeologist as well. Three generations all digging up the same past.

"Bit of a coincidence, don't you think?"

"After sixty years?" The photographer made a face. "Not really." He frowned. "What are you getting at?"

"I'm not sure, but there sure does seem to be a lack of bodies. There's no sign of Pedrazzi or the Frenchman. Just like the British soldiers. Weird."

"This isn't science fiction. They either walked out of here and died in the desert or they're still here."

"Where?"

Hilts looked around the valley. Finally he nodded to himself.

"What?" asked Finn.

"Pedrazzi took off from the old Italian airfield at Al-Kufrah. According to the reports he and DeVaux were heading off to finish a survey of some rock formation along the border with French Equatorial Africa. It was supposed to have been clear and sunny. Perfect flying weather, but a couple of hours later, which is about right, this huge sandstorm came up out of nowhere."

"What are you getting at?"

"Look," he said and pointed down toward the floor of the valley. "What do you see?"

"Nothing."

"Look closer."

She did, and after a moment she saw it. Tracks again, different than the others. Two long lines separated by six or seven feet, with a much narrower line running between them. The tracks ran off into the distance at the far end of the barren valley. Again Finn shaded her eyes against the burning sun. A hot wind was beginning to blow, sending grit into the air. She felt it now in her nostrils and her hair.

"The Waco is a tail-wheel plane just like the Wilga we flew here in. It leaves a track just like that."

"I don't get it. How can the tracks be down there and the plane crashed up here?"

"Because those tracks were from a previous visit," said Hilts. "Pedrazzi had been here before."

"So they weren't on some kind of survey flight after all."

"No, which means they'd found something they didn't want anyone else to know about."

"There's nothing here."

"There has to be. Pedrazzi, disappearing soldiers, crashed airplanes. Too many coincidences for one anonymous old streambed in the middle of nowhere. And now Adamson and his friends."

"So what are we looking for?" Finn asked.

"At a guess I'd say a cave," Hilts answered, looking up at the rock walls, "but that doesn't make much sense either." He paused. "Unless…"

"Unless what?"

"This is all sandstone. Caves usually form by water action in limestone. There hasn't been water here in a long time."

"So what are you thinking?"

"I'm thinking about Qumran."

"The Dead Sea Scrolls?" Finn frowned. "They were written by the Essenes or somebody like that."

"Essenes or Copts, it doesn't really make any difference here… but the Qumran caves were used specifically to hide the scrolls from people who wanted to destroy them, and the caves were artificial… holes dug into the stone. When the people who hid the scrolls left Qumran, they walled the cave up and covered the entrances with rubble."

"You're saying they did the same thing here?"

"Pedrazzi found something, and those soldiers must be somewhere. It's a good bet."

"What are we looking for?" asked Finn.

"An overhang, a shadow that doesn't look right, something that looks a little too geometric, squared off."

"That's nice and vague," she said and grinned.

"Best I can do."

They began to search.

It was Finn who spotted it: a combination of all three clues. Halfway up the far side slope of the canyon was a jutting overhang of darker sandstone, and directly beneath it something that looked like a broken vertical line of shadow that was simply too geometric to have been an accident of nature. Climbing the slope, they eventually reached an almost invisible ledge, barely two feet wide, and the narrow remains of a cave entrance that had been bricked up and sanded over long ago. Somewhere along the line, hundreds of years ago, there must have been some kind of seismic activity and one side of the mud brick wall had crumbled and collapsed, leaving an opening. Later a sandstorm or a small collapse of the overhang had disguised and almost flossed the entrance once again.

Sweating, Finn and Hilts stooped in front of the hole in the rock and peered in.

"Can't see much," said Hilts.

"Let's go in," Finn answered eagerly.

Hilts put a hand on her arm, stopping her.

"Hang on," he said. "Caves in the desert can be occupied."

"By what?"

Gripping the overhang with one hand and putting the other hand on Finn's shoulder to balance himself,

Hilts lifted his left leg and hammered his foot into the ancient masonry wall that blocked the entrance. He did it a second time and a large chunk of the wall crumbled inward, raising a sudden cloud of dust. There was a quick, scurrying sound like leaves rustling and then a hundred pale, crablike shapes streamed out of the cave, clicking and scraping over Finn's hiking boots. She yelped, rearing back, and almost fell off the ledge as the six-inch-long creatures raced away and disappeared.

"*L. quinquestriatus,*" said Hilts. "The Death Stalker Scorpion. One of the world's most lethal. They like cool, dark places during the daytime. They come out to hunt at night."

Finn nodded silently, gritting her teeth. Even the memory of the sound they'd made was terrifying. She stayed well back from the opening.

"Now what?"

"We go in," he said. "The wall collapsing will have scared them off."

"What if there's still some in there?"

"Step on them."

Grinning, Hilts ducked his head and entered the cave. Swallowing hard, Finn went in after him.

Kicking in the old masonry had flooded the chamber with light. Originally it had obviously been no more than a small concave depression beneath the overhang, offering a respite from the beating rays of the sun. In some indeterminate past ancient tools had been used to deepen the declivity into an oven-shaped depression in the rocks. Once a secret repository for an ancient library, like the caves at Qumran on the shores of the Dead Sea, the chamber here had become a crypt in more modern times.

Five mummified corpses, all still wearing the tattered remnants of their Long Range Desert Group uniforms, were huddled in one corner. Two were curled into whimpering fetal positions. One looked as though it had been frozen on hands and knees, half draped over an altarlike stone. Another was seated with its back against one wall, and the fifth was lying facedown, half covered by the rubble Hilts had kicked over it, one spindly, ropy arm gripping what appeared to be a verdigris-covered copper cylinder. The top of the cylinder was gone and the vase was empty. The back of the cave was a sloping pile of sand remaining after a collapse sometime in the distant past.

"The missing soldiers," murmured Hilts. He bent down and began to carefully go through what was left of the uniform of the dried-out corpse clutching the copper vase. "Careful of the ordnance, some of it could still be live." There were weapons scattered all around the cave, old Enfield rifles, a huge Lewis machine gun, a Thompson, and half a dozen or more Mills grenades.

"I wonder how they died," said Finn. "It looks like it was sudden."

Hilts shifted the leg of the dried-out corpse he was searching, revealing the desiccated shells of half a dozen creatures like the ones that had scuttled over Finn's boots.

"Disturbed a nest of scorpions; maybe hundreds. It only takes one sting to kill you; they must have been hit dozens of times. Not a pleasant way to go." He shrugged. "They wouldn't have had much time except to die."

Hilts pulled an old billfold out of an inner pocket of the man's blouse and eased it open. The papery remains of the man's organs lay like dust in the bony hollow of his rib cage.

"Anything interesting?" Finn asked.

"Bar chit from Shepherd's Hotel, membership card to the Victory Club. Library pass for the Haddon Library, Cambridge." He dug deeper into the wallet. "Here's his ID card. Professor George Pocock, Strategic Operations Executive, Grey Pillars, Cairo. That was HQ, if I remember right."

"The Haddon is the Cambridge Archaeology Faculty Library. That's where my dad met my mom."

"The Strategic Operations Executive were spies," he said. "This guy wasn't Long Range Desert Group at all."

"An archaeologist and a spy, sent out to find Pedrazzi?"

"Looks that way."

Hilts dropped the man's wallet into the pocket of his fatigue jacket, paused long enough to take several pictures, and then stood up and went to the rear of the cave. Finn, suddenly feeling almost desperately claustrophobic, went to the entrance of the narrow cave and looked down into the little valley. Nothing had moved and nothing had changed in the warlike diorama laid out below except for the whirling sand billowed up by the freshening wind that was beginning to moan through the canyon. The sky overhead had gone from harsh metallic blue to an ugly saffron color, like an old bruise. The weather was changing. She turned to tell Hilts and saw that he had uncovered something. Faintly uneasy, she turned away and went to the rear of the cave, her eyes scanning the floor for any sign of movement. Reaching Hilts she saw that he had uncovered the top and side of a large stone box. It was rectangular, four feet high, three wide, and appeared to be about six feet long, its front end angled toward the entrance. Carved into the stone was something that looked like the head of Medusa, the hair a mass of writhing snakes. Around the head, like the letters on a coin, was a faint inscription, almost worn away.

"I can't read it," Hilts said.

Finn uncapped her canteen, poured water into her palm and swept her hand around the inscription with a quick wiping motion. The letters darkened, instantly readable.

"Neat," said Hilts, admiringly. He read the words aloud: *"Hic Latito Lux Excito—Vox Luciferus."* He shook his head. "Too bad I never took Latin in school."

"I did," said Finn. "My parents insisted. According to them nothing beat a classical education. Good for reading the inscriptions on important old buildings."

"So what does it say?"

"Here Lies Hidden the Bringer of Light: The Words of Lucifer."

"You've got to be kidding," said Hilts.

"Non ioco est," she answered. "No joke."

"Lucifer, as in *the* Lucifer?"

"Lucifer was a fairly common name in ancient Rome. It didn't have the same negative connotation a few thousand years ago."

"So some Roman named Lucifer is buried inside this thing?"

"His words, anyway."

"Let's see."

Hilts used both hands to scoop the fall of sand away from the top of the box.

"We're going to open it?"

96

"It looks to me like a lot of people went to a lot of trouble to find this thing, whatever it is. The least we can do is have a look."

"What about Adamson and his pals?" Finn asked, frowning.

Hilts checked his watch.

"At least another half hour. We can be out of here long before that."

It took another five minutes to clear all the sand away from the top of the stone box. When that was done Hilts took a ten-inch "pig sticker" spike bayonet from one of the abandoned Enfield rifles and hammered it with the palm of his hand into the faint crack between the box and its heavy top. He twisted slowly and the top slid fractionally to one side, releasing a puff of stale, dusty air. Together Hilts and Finn manhandled the top of the ossuary to one side and then let it slide down to the floor of the cave, leaning against the side of the stone box. Both of them peered inside.

Stuffed into the heavy stone coffin was the bent figure of a man. He was wearing pale green trousers, a long buttoned jacket the same color, and heavy boots. The face was a leathery brown, but except for a missing ear the general structure of the face was relatively intact. Perched askew on the hawklike nose was a pair of wire-rimmed glasses. The ear was missing because there was a ragged hole in the right temple big enough to put a fist inside. Part of the jaw was missing as well, showing off a mouthful of yellow teeth. The tongue had shrunken to a black lump. Lying between the legs of the naturally mummified corpse was a copper urn like the one being gripped by the dead man near the cave entrance. Finn reached into the box and took out the small vase. Like the one in the dead archaeologist's hands, this one was empty. Hilts began going through the pockets of the brass-buttoned fatigue jacket the corpse was wearing.

"Looks like a uniform," said Finn.

"It is," Hilts answered. "Italian Desert Forces. No insignia or anything. No rank."

"There's a ring," said Finn. Gingerly she lifted the right hand. A gold band still shone on the leathery hook of the index finger. It fell off into her palm. "There's a crest engraved into it."

"Five will get you ten it's Pedrazzi. Hold on."

"Find something?"

"He was a smoker." Hilts grunted. "Lung cancer would have gotten him if somebody hadn't blown his head off." He tossed her a small faded cigarette tin. She could still see the enameled illustration of a reclining woman and the name Fatima.

Faintly, more a sense of vibration than a sound, Finn heard something in the distance, rising over the moaning of the wind.

"What's that?" she asked nervously.

Hilts paused in his examination and listened, frowning in concentration.

"Shit!" It was the first time Finn had heard him swear.

"What?"

"Chopper."

"Adamson?"

"It's some kind of gunship." He ran to the cave entrance and peered out. Finn joined him. She couldn't see anything except the blowing sand and the old vehicles on the floor of the valley. The sound was getting louder, a deep throbbing tone now. Hilts nodded grimly. "Russian. A Mil-24. It's the creep in the beret."

"Colonel Nasif."

"Must be."

"What's he doing here?"

"I doubt if we're going to be given the opportunity to ask."

"What do we do?"

"Run."

16

They made it to the ruined Italian Sahariane before the insect-like Russian-built helicopter gunship appeared. The Mil-24 slipped suddenly over the canyon wall like some mechanical horror from a science-fiction film, a hovering steel mantis, twisting beneath its main rotor, searching for its prey, bland in its pale camouflage. It moved into the valley with agonizing slowness, tilted slightly, nose down, swinging left to right.

"They haven't seen us," said Hilts.

"They must know we're here; they would have seen the plane," said Finn. They were crouched together behind the huge fender of the old truck.

"They know we're in the valley, but that's all," the pilot said, shouting into her ear over the thundering roar of the Mil's jet engine. "We've still got a chance."

As the helicopter cruised slowly along above the valley, they moved behind the Sahariane, keeping the bulk of the vehicle between them as a shield. Reaching the rear of the blasted desert vehicle, Finn looked over her shoulder. The entrance to the canyon was at least a hundred feet away; too much exposure.

"We need a distraction," she shouted.

Hilts nodded. He reached into the deep pocket of his fatigue jacket and pulled out one of the old Mills grenades from the cave.

"Think it'll work?!"

"Only one way to find out!" He pulled the pin and waited, keeping the spring lever tightly enclosed in his fist. He waited until the Mil had settled onto the ground, facing away from them, then hurled the baseball-sized grenade. The scored steel fragmentation bomb sailed up and out, the lever spinning away, glinting in the sun as it popped off the side of the grenade.

"Count to four, then head for the canyon," Hilts instructed. "I'll be right behind you!" He pulled a second grenade from his pocket and threw that one as well, aiming for the other side of the valley.

Finn, crouching, did a quick four count then leapt up and ran, keeping her eyes on the dark shadow that marked the canyon entrance. She reached the canyon just as the first grenade exploded. She tried to look back over her shoulder but felt Hilts's palm in her back, pushing her forward into the entrance. She stumbled and his hand was on her arm, pulling her up. The second grenade went off with a sharp bang and then she was in darkness.

"Go! Go! Go!" Hilts yelled, and she went. Behind her there was a harsh coughing sound as the engine of the Mil hesitated, then caught, then hesitated again. "I think I hit the rotor!" said Hilts.

Finn nodded blindly and kept on running, finally coming out of the narrow canyon entranceway and into the open desert. The little airplane stood waiting a few hundred feet away. There was no sign of the helicopter.

She stopped, horrified, staring to the left, into the desert. Rising like a brutal wave was a dark curtain a thousand feet high, blotting out the sun.

"Look!"

"Sandstorm!" Hilts yelled. "Get to the plane!"

Finn ran harder, lungs bursting, heart hammering in her chest. Her breath came in harsh, hot gasps. She reached the shadow of the wing, ducked under it and wrenched open the door of the little airplane. The wind blowing against her back was fiercely hot and filled with grains of sand that burned, stinging into her exposed skin, even tearing at her hands. The sound of it against the wings and fuselage was like the frantic tapping of a million bony fingers foretelling her choking, blast-furnace end in the immense dark thing that loomed behind her like a gargantuan, living creature, the desert's own spawn or demon.

She threw herself into the plane and scrambled to shut the door as Hilts climbed in beside her. He immediately began going through his preflight routine, reaching up to hit the button on the flap selector switch, then punching the air bottle valve between the seats and the fuel primer simultaneously. The radial engine started with a roar. He released the brake and pushed the throttle forward hard with his left hand, his right holding on to the steering column. The oversize propeller windmilled, seeming almost to suck them forward, the wall of the cliff directly in front of them.

"Aren't you going to turn?!" Finn yelled, staring at the cliff less than two hundred yards away.

"Too slow! She turns like she's sleepwalking!" he answered, pushing the throttle forward even harder. They raced across the hard-packed sand, the steamroller of the sandstorm coming up on Finn's right, filling her entire field of vision.

"Are we going to make it?!"

"Think elevating thoughts!"

The helicopter came over the top of the cliff and swooped down directly in front of them. Finn could see a spurt of flame from the twin-barreled turret gun slung under the nose and suddenly the ground immediately in front of their little plane was torn to ribbons.

Hilts jerked the steering column hard to the right, slammed his foot down on the right rudder pedal and pushed the throttle forward as far as it would go. The plane swung to the right and leapt into the air, the Mil-24 sliding away to the left, heading directly into the oncoming wall of the howling storm. There was a sudden clattering sound from behind them and Finn felt as though a giant hand had grabbed the plane and shaken it. Then the sandstorm hit and they vanished into its hungry jaws.

They flew within the storm, blind, desperately climbing until they rose above the dark, roiling horror and came out into the sunlight. Below them the storm was like the surface of some black, awful sea, shot through with streaks of lightning.

"It really is a storm," said Finn, staring down.

"Crazy things," Hilts said and nodded, checking his instruments. "The friction of the sand causes the lightning. All sorts of magnetic disturbances as well."

"Down there, you flew right at that helicopter. You didn't turn."

"This thing flies like stink, but it takes a lot to turn, and anyway, the Mil-24 was probably the least maneuverable chopper the Russians ever made. Fly at it and it has to swing around in a big circle. I knew we had the throttle to get up and over."

"Knew?"

"Hoped." Hilts grinned.

"Think elevating thoughts? That was the best you could come up with?"

"Better than kiss your ass good-bye," said Hilts. "Which was the only other alternative."

"What about the helicopter? Will they come after us?"

"No. They didn't have enough time to get the elevation. That Nasif guy's going to have to ride it out on the ground. Even then he might have to radio for help to get restarted."

"So now what do we do? We can't go back to the dig."

"There's an old oil airfield at Ayn al Ghazal. We can fuel up there and get across the border into Egypt."

"And after that?"

"We'll have to give that some thought. Cairo. The embassy. New passports. Maybe talk to your pal Mickey Hearts."

"Or see if we can find out what Pedrazzi was up to."

"Should have brought one of those copper urns with you," said Hilts.

"I was distracted," Finn answered. She dug into the pocket of her jacket and pulled out the old flat cigarette tin with the lounging woman on the lid. "All we've got is this."

"And neither one of us smokes," Hilts said. "Darn." They were flying due east now, toward the distant border, away from the sandstorm and the threat of Nasif and his helicopter.

Finn shook the tin but there was no sound. For an empty tin it seemed heavy. Curious, she pried open the lid and was surprised to see a wadded piece of dusty linen inside. Hilts glanced across the narrow cockpit.

"Got something?"

"I'm not sure," she said. "It looks like a handkerchief."

"I'm taking us down under the radar," said Hilts, gently easing the control stick forward. The plane responded instantly, swooping down toward the desert. "Wouldn't want our friend calling in the cavalry on us."

Finn unwrapped the cloth. There was a monogram in one corner, two letters entwined beneath a crest. "L.P. Lucio Pedrazzi. The crest is the same as the ring he was wearing."

"He didn't get that hole in the side of his head from a scorpion bite," said Hilts. "A handgun from close range, more likely."

"Murdered?"

"At a guess, yeah."

"But according to you the only person with him was…"

"Pierre DeVaux, a monk," Hilts completed.

"A monk with a pistol?"

"Agatha Christie would have loved it."

Finn finished unwrapping the handkerchief. In the center of the fabric square a gold medallion gleamed. Staring up at Finn was the embossed malevolent face of a frowning Medusa, lips snarling, hair a mass of writhing snakes.

"A coin?" asked Hilts, looking at the object in her palm.

"A medallion."

"What does it have written around the head?"

"The inscription is the same as the one of the stone coffin," she said. "*Hic Latito Lux Excito—Vox Luciferus.* Here Lies Hidden the Bringer of Light: The Words of Lucifer."

She turned the golden disk over. Engraved on the other side was the profile of a handsome face and another inscription.

"What does it say?"

"*Legio III Africanus—Domus in Venosa est.* Third African Legion, whose home is in Venosa," she translated.

Hilts's brow furrowed. "Where's Venosa?"

17

Venosa is a town of some twelve thousand citizens scattered around a volcanic hilltop in the district of Basilicata, a small, out-of-the-way *regione* that lies roughly in the arch of Italy's boot, bounded by the Gulf of Taranto to the south and the marble spine of the Apennine Mountains to the north. The architecture is bland, whitewashed stucco competing with beige stone and dusty, red-tiled roofs. Few tourists go there; it has none of the flavors of Tuscany or the grandeur of Rome, but once, a long time ago and under another name, it was one of the assembly points along the Appian Way for the great legions of Rome as they went out to conquer the world. Today it has a number of relatively unimportant churches, several sets of catacombs, a fort, and one good restaurant, Il Grifo, located in the center of town, just off the small central square.

Finn parked the little blue Fiat Panda in the cramped town square and switched off the engine. The only difference between the square and a utilitarian cobblestone parking lot was a medium-sized statue of an old Roman in a toga with a scroll in one hand and wearing an olive wreath on his half-bald head. Presumably this was the town's best-known famous son, Quintus Horatius Flaccus, better known in literary history as the poet Horace. Finn was the one behind the wheel because she spoke the language fluently, having spent a year in Florence gathering research for her master's thesis on the drawings of Michelangelo. It was also a practical way of dealing with the relentlessly chauvinistic *polizia* on the highways, who were always willing to give a pretty red-haired tourist a break; especially one who could say *per favore* and *grazie* with such a charming accent.

Finn popped open the door of the miniscule little vehicle.

"Stay here," she instructed.

"Why?" asked Hilts, undoing his seat belt.

"In this country a woman asking questions by herself works better than if she's with someone," Finn answered. "Italian men are all the same—they think they were born to please women and that we're all damsels in distress and desperate for a man's attention. You'd be competition, at least in their minds."

"What if it's an old guy?"

"Even better," she said and grinned. "Something to prove."

"What if he's gay?"

"He'd still want to pinch me, just to keep up the national honor."

"Doesn't say much for the feminist cause."

She laughed. "There's the feminist cause and then there's Italy."

Finn climbed out of the car and crossed the claustrophobic little square. She entered the local *Municipio*, or City Hall, a square, crumbling stone building with an entrance like a missing tooth and no distinguishing architectural features of any kind. Hilts settled back in his seat and picked up the guidebook they'd bought twelve miles back at a gas station in Rapolla.

According to the book the town had been called Venusia a couple of thousand years ago, named after the Roman goddess of beauty. These days the most important thing in town was the tomb of the wife of Robert Guiscard, the man who conquered Sicily, the reason the Mafia was invented in the first place and the origin of the word "wise-acre." As far as Hilts could tell there was nothing here to connect with Lucio Pedrazzi and a cave full of late-model mummies in the Libyan Desert. On the other hand, it was the only clue they had.

Five minutes later Finn reappeared and got back into the car.

"So?" asked Hilts.

"Believe it or not, his name was Alberto Pacino and he insisted on doing bad imitations from *Scarface* in an Italian accent."

"So other than saying hello to his little friend, did you find out anything?"

"I didn't say hello to his little friend, but I found out who the resident history guy is in the town. His name is Signore Abramo Vergadora. He's a retired professor and he lives in a place called Villa Embreo Errante, a few miles north.

"Embreo Errante?"

"The Wandering Jew," translated Finn.

18

Signore Vergadora's villa was located in a pleasant shaded valley between two of the seemingly endless number of rocky hills that rose throughout the area like overgrown piles of discarded dirt thrown up by some gigantic dog searching for an old buried bone. Unlike most of the valleys they'd driven through, this one actually seemed capable of growing something. The villa was located in an olive grove, and off to one side a brook meandered pleasantly through the trees. The villa itself was reasonably modest and very old, yellowed stucco peeling away from ancient stone, the deep windows covered with wrought-iron gratings, the roof dusty red with terra-cotta tiles, a central tower in front standing guard above the rest of the sprawling building.

Finn parked in front of the main door, and she and Hilts climbed out of the car and into the bright, warm sunlight. Finn could hear the brook now, babbling quietly to itself, and the afternoon breeze rustling through the poplars that stood around the house like sentries, much taller than the gnarled grove of olives that might have been here as long as the house, perhaps centuries.

They stood in front of the heavy planked front door and Finn pulled the bell chain. From somewhere deep inside the villa there was a faint tinkling sound and then the shuffle of approaching feet. A moment later the door creaked open and a face appeared: an Italian J.R.R. Tolkien wearing a yarmulke pinned to unruly silver hair, drooping bags beneath twinkling eyes, and rosy cheeks forced down by time and gravity on either side of an almost feminine mouth that looked as though it rarely frowned. The man had bright red reading glasses perched on his forehead and wore a brown corduroy suit much too warm for the summer, complete with vest, white shirt and tie, the vest decorated with a fob and chain that spanned a moderate belly. He wore purple velvet bedroom slippers.

"Ah," he said happily, "you are the American couple."

"How'd you know that?" Hilts asked.

"Alberto called me from the *Municipio,*" the old man answered, still smiling. "That one thinks every American is a Hollywood producer looking for new stars." He stepped aside and gestured them forward. "Come in, please. My name is Abramo Vergadora."

Vergadora took them through several high-ceilinged underfurnished rooms, finally ushering them into what was obviously his sanctum sanctorum, a library, the walls lined with overflowing bookshelves, the stone floor covered with overlapping Persian carpets. The room was laid out with a dozen chairs and couches, with more tables and chairs piled high with books and more stacks on the floor. The whole room smelled of paper, leather, cigar smoke and ash from the gigantic fireplace that stood in the corner. Finn stopped. Carved into the mantel of the fireplace was the same coat of arms she'd seen on Pedrazzi's ring and on the corner of the ancient handkerchief that had been wrapped around the gold medallion.

"That's the arms of the Pedrazzi family," she said.

Vergadora looked at her curiously.

"No, it's not," he said. "But it is extraordinary that you should know it at all."

"It is the coat of arms Lucio Pedrazzi used," she insisted.

"True, but not one that the Pedrazzi family had any right to," Vergadora replied quietly. "But before we get into any further discussions, perhaps I can offer you coffee, or tea? Lemonade? A soft drink? I only drink Dr Pepper, I'm afraid." The old man's smile widened even more. "Or perhaps something stronger. A martini? Brandy Alexander? They are the only two American drinks I know how to make, and sadly I am without domestic help with the exception of the old woman who does my laundry on Thursdays."

"Coffee would be nice," said Finn.

"Sure," said Hilts with a nod.

"Wonderful." Vergadora beamed. He turned and scuttled away, his bedroom slippers whispering into the distance.

"He's a nut bar," said Hilts. "A nice nut bar, but a nut bar nevertheless."

"I prefer the word 'eccentric,'" Finn said and smiled. She began wandering along the rows of books.

"He's got everything here from Dante's *Inferno* to *The Stand* by Stephen King."

"Not such a leap when you think about it," Hilts said, dropping down into one of the comfortable leather armchairs. He watched Finn continue her inspection of the bookshelves. "What do you think about the Pedrazzi thing?"

"I can't wait to hear his explanation," said Finn.

"He's Jewish," mused Hilts. "That's a bit strange."

"The villa's called the Wandering Jew. Historically there've been Jews in Italy for thousands of years."

"Not something you hear about much."

"Fiorello La Guardia was an Italian Jew. Modigliani, the sculptor, was a Jew. I think the guy who invented the Olivetti typewriter was Jewish."

"He was. His name was Camilo Olivetti." Vergadora came back into the room carrying a tray. In addition to the coffee there was a single budding rose in a slim, porcelain vase. He set the tray down on a table.

"I knew his son, Adriano, quite well," the old man continued. "We spent the war in Lausanne together pretending to be exiles. If he hadn't been so wealthy he would have been a communist, I'm positive."

He paused, his smile wistful. "Did you know they are the only company that still manufactures manual type-writers? I find that a comfort in a world where people have things called BlackBerries instead of address books and computers are named after fruit." He smiled at Finn. "Cream? Sugar?"

"Black," she said.

"Both," said Hilts.

Vergadora poured, then handed the cups around as Finn took a seat across the table from him.

"Tell me about Pedrazzi and the coat of arms," said Finn.

"Tell me why you wish to know," Vergadora replied.

Hilts answered. "A few days ago we found his dried-up corpse in a cave in the Libyan Desert. Someone had shot him in the head."

"How wonderful," the old man said and beamed again. "An end devoutly to be wished. He was truly an evil man." He took a sip of coffee and squinted at the rose. He adjusted the single stalk fractionally. "Did you find the remains of that *busone* DeVaux, as well?"

"No, Pedrazzi's body had been hidden away in an old ossuary," said Finn. "The only other remains were some British soldiers from years later."

"Pity. As a rabbi I'm supposed to be above that sort of thinking, but sometimes I just can't help thinking that some people should have been strangled at birth, Pierre DeVaux being very high on my list."

"You still haven't explained about the coat of arms," Finn prodded.

"What were you doing in the middle of the Libyan Desert?"

"Do you always answer questions by asking them?" asked Hilts.

"It's a rabbinical thing, a bad habit, but useful." Vergadora offered up one of his gentle smiles. "It gives an old man time to think. I'm not quite as sharp as you young people."

"Yeah, right."

"The coat of arms?" insisted Finn.

"Three hands holding crescents, three palm trees, and a lion rampant. Nothing particularly Hebraic about that in Pedrazzi's limited brain except that the duchy of Lorro, which was centered roughly where the olive grove is outside my door, used to belong to my family, the Duca di Levi Vergadora Ibn Lorro being the original holder of the title granted by the Lombard kings in the twelfth century. If Pedrazzi had done his research he would have realized that crescents, palms, and open hands were all indicators of the Jewish faith in heraldry. I was the last duke of Lorro, not that Italian titles meant much by then in any real sense, but in 1938 Mussolini decided to follow Hitler's path and Jews became persona non grata for a time. I was living outside of Italy by then, but in absentia they stripped me of the title, this house, and what land was left. It was given to Pedrazzi as a gift by Il Duce himself. Pedrazzi took his dukedom very seriously; he had the crest put on everything."

"You went to Switzerland, Lausanne," offered Finn.

"And then America after the war, then Canada, then Israel for a time. But I am as much Italian as I am a Jew, and I became homesick. I heard that the villa was for sale and I purchased what had once been mine. Pedrazzi had named it for himself, but I erased that as well."

"The Wandering Jew comes home," Hilts said and grinned.

"Something like that." Vergadora nodded. He finished his coffee and set the cup back on the tray. He sat back in his chair, dug into his pocket for an old briar pipe, and lit it using a kitchen match he took from the other pocket and struck with his thumbnail. The old man puffed, the pipe sucking with a noisy gurgle. He looked more like Tolkien than ever. "So," he said, once the pipe was fuming and sending up clouds of aromatic smoke toward the nicotine-colored ceiling. "You seemed surprised to see my family crest over the fireplace, ergo, that is not the reason you came here. Since you are American and have recently been in the Libyan Desert, I can only presume that you were part of that buffoon Rolf Adamson's so-called archaeological expedition that has been so much in the news of late. Yes?"

"So-called?" said Finn.

"Rolf Adamson has the somewhat limited archaeological credentials of a man digging a cesspool in his back garden."

"I can see you don't mind sharing your opinions," Hilts said with a laugh.

"Archaeology is serious business, young man," said Vergadora, using the stem of his pipe to emphasize the point. "As somebody once said, the blueprint of the past often provides a road map for the future."

"If you don't know where you've been, how can you know where you're going?" Hilts responded.

It was the old man's turn to laugh.

"He who forgets the past is doomed to repeat it."

"How about this one—'Archaeology is the search for fact... not truth. If it's truth you're looking for, Dr. Tyree's philosophy class is right down the hall,'" Hilts quoted.

"Now you're making fun of me," puffed Vergadora, laughing even harder.

"You're both crazy," said Finn. She reached into her pocket, took out the old cigarette tin, and slid it across the table toward the white-haired old man. He looked at the picture of the woman on the lid for a moment, then popped open the tin. Pedrazzi's old handkerchief had been replaced by a square of cotton batten from a drugstore. Vergadora stared at the gleaming medallion, then carefully turned it over and looked at the obverse side.

"This is the reason we came to Venosa," said Finn.

"Oh dear," the old man murmured.

"Oh dear?"

"Young Luciferus Africanus and his mythical legion."

"Mythical?"

"There is very little factual evidence that he ever existed, let alone his legion. When Rome fell, so did its bureaucracy, I'm afraid. There are scattered references here and there, but not much more than a hint. He was a legionary in Judea at the time of Jesus, that much is known. Some credit him as being the Roman who guarded Christ's tomb and witnessed the Resurrection. Others credit him as the source for Lloyd C. Douglas's novel *The Robe*. He's also supposed to be the man who led the Lost Legion into the desert, and Almasy thought he was the source of the legends about the blond, blue-eyed men who were the guardians of Zerzura."

"In other words he's anyone you want him to be."

"Basically, yes." He glanced at the medallion again. "Although this would seem to take him out of the realm of myth… if it's genuine."

"How can you tell if it's the real thing?" Hilts asked.

"Difficult," the old man said and shrugged. "Gold is extremely hard to date accurately. Someone melting down gold objects from the appropriate era and using Roman gravity casting methods from the time period would have little difficulty forging such an object."

"It was in Pedrazzi's pocket when we found his body."

"So much for provenance then," the old man said, snorting. "If ever there was a man who could rightfully be charged with falsifying data, it would be him." He shook his head. "On top of that there are the other legends."

"What other legends?"

"The legends of the Luciferians and the Lucifer Gospel."

"The Luciferians?" Finn asked.

"Sounds devilish," said Hilts.

"Please," sighed Finn.

"The Luciferians were a schismatic group within the Catholic Church during the late fourth century. They followed the teachings of a man named Lucifer Calaritanus, who was a bishop in Sardinia. Lucifer had once been a follower of Arius, a quite important theologian who argued that Christ was not part of the godhead but only a mortal expression of it. Some people, Pedrazzi included, thought that Luciferus Africanus was the namesake of Lucifer Calaritanus, the bishop. There's a lot of Freemasonry and idiocy about the Knights Templar involved, which Pedrazzi embraced fervently of course, since much of it was the mythic foundations of Nazism. All that silliness with Beowulf and Wagner and the *Übermensch*. Your friend Pedrazzi even thought there was a connection between Arius the heretic and 'Aryan,' the racial term invented by lunatics like the Frenchman, the conte de Gobineau, and his English friend Houston Stewart Chamberlain."

"Never heard of either one," Hilts said.

"Hitler did. He used Gobineau's *An Essay on the Inequality of the Human Races* as a blueprint for *Mein Kampf* and the Final Solution. It described the concept of a concentration camp perfectly, among other things. The French may have invented the idea of Liberty, Equality and Brotherhood, but sadly it was a Frenchman, not a German, who also invented Nazism, I'm afraid. Chamberlain was one on his acolytes. He came up with an amusing theory that Christ was somehow not Jewish.

Hitler called his good friend Herr Chamberlain the Prophet of the Reich."

"The original white supremacist," said Finn.

"Yes," the old man said and nodded.

"What do you know about the man who was with him when he disappeared? DeVaux," asked Hilts.

"Another Frenchman. Trained at the École Biblique in Jerusalem. Personal private secretary to Cardinal Maglione when he was papal nuncio in France, continued with him for the rest of his career both as Vatican secretary of state under Pacelli, Pius XII, and also interestingly enough as Grand Chancellor of the Pontifical Institute of Christian Archaeology."

"What exactly does that mean?" Finn asked.

"DeVaux had a great deal to do with all things archaeological within the Church. It's well enough known that at the time certain elements within the Vatican were looking for archaeological justifications for some of the things Hitler and Mussolini were extolling. The Spear of Destiny, the Ark of the Covenant, Ultima Thule, or Atlantis. Also at the time one of the great fears was the establishment of a Jewish State in Palestine. DeVaux and a lot of other Franciscans were afraid that their hegemony over the Holy Land would come to an end if that happened." The old man smiled around the stem of his pipe. "And just to make things interesting, Maglione, DeVaux's boss, DeVaux himself, and Pedrazzi were all members in good standing of the Knights of Malta."

"Who were they?" asked Hilts.

"You've seen the *Godfather* movies presumably?"

"Sure."

"Our friend Tony Montana at the *Municipio* in Venosa can quote from all three extensively. You remember in the last of them that Al Pacino is given a medal?"

"Vaguely."

"It is the cross of Saint Sebastian. He is being made a Knight of Malta. It is indicative, I think."

"Is that anything like the Templars?" Finn asked.

"They *are* the Templars. There were two parts to the order when it was formed—the Hospitallers, the ones who cared for the sick, who wore black, and the Military order, who wore white in the manner of the Cistercians."

Hilts looked amused. "We're talking Dan Brown, *The Da Vinci Code,* all that?"

"I'm afraid so," Vergadora said with a nod. "But these men are no joke. In recent years the Fraterninty of Saint Sebastian has returned to its paramilitary roots. They are zealots, trained like marines and utterly obedient. They even have a website: www.christiansoldiers.org. These are not people to be taken lightly."

"They sound like they could be friends of Rolf Adamson," said Hilts.

"They certainly share the same basic philosophy," the old man said. "Which I'm afraid brings me to the last piece of mythology associated with your legionary, Luciferus Africanus." Vergadora reached out and touched the medallion. "Do either of you know the story of the Seven Sleepers?"

"Never heard of it," said Hilts. Finn just shook her head.

"It is undoubtedly the source of your own fairy tale of Rip Van Winkle. Gregory of Tours discusses it during the sixth century, but it was well known before that. There are several versions, but the basic story is this: seven youths in the time of the Roman emperor Decius refused to honor his decree and repent of their belief in the Resurrection. They were walled into a cave but did not die. Instead they slept for two centuries, woke up to show that the Resurrection of the flesh was possible, then slept again until the coming of the Messiah. They sleep there still, these seven warriors, in a cave of immense riches, somewhere beyond the Western Sea."

"Beyond the Western Sea?" said Hilts.

"The U.S.," said Finn.

"Exactly," the old man said, nodding.

"A treasure cave in the United States—that really is Adamson territory."

"And the territory of his grandfather, the Reverend Schuyler Grand."

"You've heard of him?" said Hilts, obviously surprised.

"My boy," the old man said pleasantly, "if you live long enough your hearing begins to fade but you wind up hearing everything."

Finn laughed at the small joke but she found herself thinking of Arthur Simpson in her hotel room and his warning about Senator Jimmy "Sword of the Lord" Judd and his Tenth Crusade militia.

Hilts stood. "Coffee went right through me, I'm afraid. Can I use your facilities?"

"Certainly. There's a powder room just down the hallway by the kitchen." He stood. "I'll show you."

"I can find it," Hilts said. "No problem." He left the room.

Finn looked at the gleaming medallion on the table in front of her. The connections were becoming frighteningly obvious, but the final intent remained obscure. What was Rolf Adamson's real objective in all of this and just how far was he willing to go to accomplish it?

"What would this DeVaux person gain by killing Pedrazzi?" Finn asked.

"Silence, I suspect," murmured Vergadora. "He clearly had a different agenda."

"I wonder if he got out of the desert alive? The plane was a wreck," she said.

"Perhaps it was always his intention that Pedrazzi would die that day," suggested the old man. He used another match to light his pipe again, then looked at her above the smoking bowl. "Perhaps he had some other means of transportation at hand."

Hilts reappeared.

"Possible," he said, sitting down again. "With the right vehicle and enough water it wouldn't have been too difficult for a man who knew the desert."

"DeVaux accompanied Almasy on one expedition between the wars and he was with Bagnold on several of his expeditions."

"Bagnold?"

"The man who organized the Long Range Desert Group; those men in the scorpion cave."

"Quite right," said Vergadora. "DeVaux and Bagnold were at Cambridge together. That's where they met."

Cambridge, thought Finn. Arthur Simpson, her father, DeVaux, and this man Bagnold, all sharing a single thread. Were there others? She had another thought, this one far removed from Cambridge University.

"Was Lucio Pedrazzi from Venosa?"

"That's rather an interesting question," said Vergadora. "And the answer to it is no. Pedrazzi's family were orphans of the Papal States; his family were *burocrates* in the commune of Pontecorvo, just south of Rome, until Napoleon threw them out."

"Then why did he come here? Was there something between your families?"

"Not that I'm aware of. He had an interest in the Jewish catacombs here, that I do know."

"And DeVaux?"

"The inscriptions in the Benedictine abbey were his specialty. The abbey and the Church of the Trinity are built on the ruins of the catacombs." The old man made a sour face. "Unfortunately access is controlled by the Vatican. They say one need only apply to the custodian in Rome, but it seems the custodian is never available for such applications. It has been that way ever since I can remember."

"Could Luciferus Africanus have been buried there?"

"If he was a Jew, which is doubtful. The legate or the tribune of a Roman legion was usually of the senator class; not a group known for keeping kosher."

"I'm getting a headache," said Finn. "Too much information all at once." That and her growing suspicions about Vergadora, not to mention the clouds of smoke from the old man's pipe.

"So there would be no point in trying to get into the catacombs, is that what you're saying?" Hilts asked, ignoring Finn's comment.

"None whatsoever," the old man replied. "Unless you have some facility with ancient Greek, Latin, and the occasional inscription in Aramaic. The only person who ever knew much about them was an old man named Mueller, one of my teachers. Even DeVaux only scratched the surface, at least as I understand it."

"Then I guess we've reached a dead end," said Finn. All she wanted to do now was leave, to have some time to think about everything that had happened during the last few days.

"Perhaps so," said the old man. "It depends of course on what you were trying to accomplish in the first place."

"We want to find out why everyone's so interested in this Lucifer Africanus guy for one thing," said Hilts. He stood up, walked to the table and picked up the cigarette case, snapping it shut over the medallion. "Interested enough to kill for sixtyfive years ago, and interested enough to kill for now." He handed the old tin box to Finn, who dropped it back into the pocket of her jacket.

Vergadora peered up at them over his glasses from the other side of the table and slipped the pipe out of his mouth. He pushed a nicotine-yellow thumb into the bowl, tamping down the plug of ash and tobacco.

"My suggestion would be to abandon your quest before your curiosity kills you like it did Pedrazzi," the white-haired gentleman cautioned. There was something in his voice now other than the soft tones of a retired professor. The warning sounded more like a threat, and a threat with something dark and menacing behind it. "Old secrets are like old wounds; they fester."

"How long have you worked for Mossad?" asked Hilts flatly.

"You mean *Hamossad Le'mode'in U'le'tafkidim Meyuchadim*, the Institute for Coordination? Israeli Intelligence?" The old man smiled. "Believe me, young man, I really am nothing more than a retired university professor."

"Sure you are," said Hilts. He turned to Finn. "I think we should be going."

Finn stood.

"Thank you for your help, signore," she said, and held out her hand.

Vergadora climbed to his feet. He shook her hand, his grip strong and firm. "You are traveling in dangerous seas," he said. "It would be a shame if you were hurt in a battle that was not yours to fight."

"Maybe you're right," she replied. He seemed sincere enough, but again there was an undertone of threat in the old man's voice.

He walked them to the door and stood at the entrance as they climbed back into their rental car, and watched them as they drove away down the long drive that ran between the poplars and through the ancient grove of olive trees. Then he turned and went back into the villa.

19

"So what do you make of all of that?" Hilts asked as they drove away.

"I'm not sure," said Finn, gearing down as she made the turn off Vergadora's drive, then up again as the car reached the main road. "I wasn't kidding, all that talk gave me a headache."

"A lot of it was just that, talk," grunted Hilts. He tapped his fingers on the dashboard angrily. "The old man's very good at his job, I'll give him that."

"What job?"

"Leading us down the garden path. All that crap about Pedrazzi. He knows something about what Adamson's up to in the here and now. Forget about the past."

"What was that about him working for Israeli Intelligence? That's a bit of a stretch, isn't it—just because he's Jewish?"

"It's not because he's Jewish, it's about what he knows—how well and how much. Not to mention the fact that there aren't too many people around who know the original name of the Mossad. Nobody's called it the Institute for Coordination since the fifties. A retired history professor who knows that much about the current state of the intelligence community is more than just a retired history professor. I'm pretty sure he's at least a *sayan,* if not something else."

"What's that?"

"The *sayanim* are Israeli 'sleepers,' all over the world, in all walks of life, ready to help an operation at a moment's notice. He fits the profile perfectly." Hilts shook his head. "He even has his pal Al Pacino at City Hall as an early-warning system."

"Why would he warn us off that way?" Finn asked. "He hasn't been hanging around in his villa for all these years waiting for us."

"Not us," said Hilts. "Anybody who came along showing interest in Pedrazzi or the rest of the story."

"But why?" Finn insisted. "It's ancient history. When you get right down to it, does anybody really care about some man who commanded a legion two thousand years ago?"

"The operative date is two thousand years ago. Most of the Western world, the U.S. in particular, sets its watch by that particular clock. The Catholic Church is based on it."

"Sure," Finn said and laughed, easing her foot off the gas as they came up behind an ancient tractor pulling a wagonload of manure. "An old Jewish rabbi working for the Vatican."

"Add it up," said Hilts. "They tried to kill us in Cairo. A monk from Jerusalem starts sniffing around. Adamson and his pals are up to something in the desert that's not quite kosher, as Vergadora would put it. We wind up crossing paths with somebody who's playing possum in a place that's historically and recently connected to what-ever's going on. A man who's just waiting for someone to come along and say the magic words, Luciferus Africanus. A man with his own secrets."

"Such as?"

"Remember when I got up to use the bathroom back at the villa?"

"Yes."

"I wasn't using the bathroom, I was snooping."

"And?"

"Why does an old rabbi who clearly doesn't like our murderous friend from the past, Brother DeVaux, have the number of another Franciscan monk in his personal telephone book?"

"Was there an address?" Finn asked. They had reached the traffic circle for the Autostrada. They could go either west toward Rome or north to Milan.

"Yeah, there was an address."

"Where?"

"Lausanne, Switzerland. The Monastery of St. François. Where Vergadora spent the war with Signore Olivetti, remember?"

Finn turned north.

20

Finn Ryan, still fully dressed, lay on the bed in her hotel room and listened to the sounds of the sleeping city. She and Hilts had driven straight through from Venosa, stopping only once for a quick bite to eat at a roadside restaurant. The made the journey in a little less than eight hours. They spent another hour and a half getting thoroughly lost in the two-thousand-year-old metropolis, finally dumping the rental car in what seemed to be Milan's last available parking spot, then walked until they found a relatively inexpensive hotel willing to rent them rooms without reservations and almost no luggage.

The rooms turned out to be tiny, perched under the eaves on the top floor with a view out over the dusty street instead of the hotel courtyard, with its newly renovated open-air garden and restaurant. Both of them were too tired for food, so they'd simply said good night and gone to their separate rooms. But sleep had not come. She was worried, and even the warm night air seemed charged with apprehension. She longed for a bath, but to strip and slip into the welcoming heat would somehow make her too vulnerable. Visions from old Alfred Hitchcock movies swarmed through her mind like buzzing bees.

Through her open window Finn could hear the distant sound of traffic, and closer, the echoing of tapping, high-heeled footsteps on the hard cobbles of the street and the sound of shrill female laughter. Someone made a comment and the woman laughed again, while a male companion made a mocking, hooting sound. Suddenly she started as she heard the muted shriek of a train whistle cutting through the dark night air; Milan's gigantic and brutal Stazione Centrale hunched like one of Mussolini's stone nightmares only a few blocks away, the huge white granite hulk proof of the cliché that if nothing else Il Duce had made the Italian trains run on time.

Milan, Finn knew, was a smaller and considerably more decrepit version of Paris, and like Paris it was almost completely empty of skyscrapers. Scaffolding seemed to grow from buildings constantly being refurbished like permanent exoskeletons. It was the place where thirties fascism had been born, where Leonardo's and Dan Brown's *Last Supper* was doled out to ticket holders for roughly a buck and a half per minute, and it was the place where thirties fascism had finally died at an Esso station in the Piazzale Loreto with Benito Mussolini hanging from his heels while half a dozen GIs looked on. It was home to the finest Italian fashion, the most extreme Italian politics, and the best-equipped riot police in the world. It's duomo, or cathedral, was the third largest church in all of Christendom, but the city's true religion was soccer, second only to the pursuit of money. It was a city far too brash and industrious to be charming, and certainly its vast slums and sometimes choking smog were not what the average reader of the *New York Times* thought about as he dreamed of a holiday in Tuscany.

Finn jumped as her door burst open and Hilts appeared, shirt unbuttoned to the waist. His hair was all over the place and his eyes were wide and hot.

"Turn on the TV!"

"What's the matter!?"

"Just turn the damn thing on!"

Finn picked up the remote from the bedside table and pushed the ON button. The screen on the big console TV on the bureau at the end of the bed blipped on to CNN, which was the last channel she'd had on before trying to sleep. They were showing a weather map of Eastern Europe. It was raining in Prague.

"Not that! Switch it!" barked Hilts. He came into the room and closed the door. Finn did as she was told, flipping through the channels.

"There!" he said. "Hold it!"

It was channel six, Telelombardia, a local news show. A well-dressed dark-haired woman with a serious look on her face was reading a report as she stood in the middle of a futuristic set constructed of something that looked like chrome-plated scaffolding. There were keyed-in inserts showing an old black-and-white photograph of two smiling middle-aged men, one of whom looked vaguely familiar.

"Turn it up! What are they saying?"

"Calm down and I'll tell you," said Finn, using the remote to adjust the volume. She listened. The news anchor kept on with her story. Finn translated for Hilts as the story continued, thrusting her feet into her running shoes as they watched.

—*Here seen with his friend Adriano Olivetti, Vergadora was a well-known and well-liked*

*member of the academic community and a noted
historian. His sudden, violent death at the hands
of what are reported to be members of the terrorist
group* Third Position *came as a shock to the
people of Venosa, the farming community where
he made his home.—*

The scene on the television changed to an idyllic
shot of rolling hills and vineyards from the station's stock
footage library, then more footage of the town itself,
and finally a floodlit shot of the villa among the poplars,
surrounded by efficient-looking police unreeling tape
while the bubble lights on their patrol cars skipped franti-
cally over the scene. This was then shockingly overlaid by
two grainy black-and-white pictures that clearly showed
Hilts and Finn shot from a high angle standing outside the
door of the villa.

*—These pictures, taken from Rabbi Vergadora's
security system, show his attackers shortly before
the elderly professor was slaughtered in his
library...—*

"I didn't see a camera," said Finn, shocked and horrified by what she was seeing.

"They murdered him," muttered Hilts, staring at the
screen. "And they're putting it on us."

"They?"

"This is Adamson and his pals."

"You've got to be kidding!"

"You think it's a coincidence?"

"The camera got us on tape. There's been a misunder-
standing, that's all," said Finn. "We'll just go to the police
and explain."

"Where do they get this stuff about us being members of Third Position?"

"Who are they?"

"The Italian version of al-Qaeda. We're being set up."

"It's a mistake."

"It's no mistake. Vergadora is dead. If the news is saying it's Third Position, that probably means Vergadora was killed violently. Their weapon of choice is a cut-down shotgun, a Mafia *lupara*. This is not Boy Scouts, Finn. This is hardball. These people are out to kill us."

"But why kill Vergadora?"

"Because he obviously needed killing as far as they were concerned, and because blaming it on us turns you and me into lepers—untouchables. With this hanging over us there's nobody we can go to for help."

"So what are you suggesting?"

"That we get the hell out of here. Fast. We've got to regroup."

"If they've got our faces on tape they probably have a description of the car. Maybe even a plate number."

"The train station then."

On cue there was the sound of two-tone sirens wailing and the screeching of tires. Finn jumped off the bed and raced to the window. She looked out and saw the dark street below littered with blue-and-white *polizia* Alfas. A black-and-white van thundered up behind them and half a dozen special police poured out dressed in camo blouses, black helmets, and loose fatigue pants. All of them were carrying compact Beretta machine guns or short-barreled Benelli shotguns.

"SISDE," muttered Hilts, looking over her shoulder. He grabbed her wrist and pulled her away from the window.

"Who are they?"

He started dragging her toward the door. "Italian Secret Police, come on!"

"My clothes! My things!"

"No time!"

She barely had time to grab her wallet and watch off the nightstand before Hilts pushed her out into the narrow hall. There were two rooms to the left, three to the right, the same across the hall, and the single old-fashioned cage elevator in the middle. Even as they stood there the mechanism began to grind.

"Here they come!"

To the left Finn saw a backlit sign, white on red: *USCITA*. Exit.

"This way!" She pulled him left. Three seconds later and they were there. They barged through the pneumatic door. Six floors below booted footsteps hammered and shouts echoed up.

"*Su! Su!*" Hard voices yelling. Up. They were trapped. The elevator and the stairs were blocked.

"Maybe we should surrender ourselves."

"These guys are the shoot-first breed and they've got machine guns."

"There," said Finn, pointing up. "The roof!" There was a pull-down fire ladder leading to a trapdoor in the ceiling of the stairwell. Below them the pounding boots were getting closer.

Hilts jumped up, grabbed the bottom rung of the ladder, and pulled hard. It came creaking down, showering them with flecks of dried-out rustproofing paint. Hilts went up first, banging the palm of his hand into the underside of the trapdoor. It slammed open and he continued through the exit. In an instant he reappeared, holding his hand down to Finn as she climbed upward.

A few seconds later she was standing on the roof of the hotel as Hilts hauled up the ladder and dropped the trapdoor closed. The summer air was hot and heavy. There were neither stars nor moon. The night was dark except for the wash of light from the street below.

"They'll figure out where we went quickly enough when they find our rooms empty."

"Where to now?" asked Finn.

"Anywhere but here."

Milan, like many of the older European cities, began its existence behind walls, where space was always at a premium. Lawns, backyards, drive-ways, and garages simply never existed. Rome was the first city to have tenements, in the first century, and Milan wasn't far behind. By the Renaissance things were much less confined, but old habits died hard. Even beyond the walls of the Old City humanity was densely packed, building built against building so that entire blocks and neighborhoods consisted of a solid wall of terraced structures presenting a single face to the street, the rear of the buildings creating common courtyards or airshafts, sometimes connected and sometimes not.

The Hotel Caravaggio occupied a corner of such a block in the Brera district of the city, once known as the Montmartre of Milan but long since abandoned by the avante-garde artists, designers, and musicians who had once made it famous. The Caravaggio's particular block was bounded by the via Marangoni to the north, the via Locatelli to the south, and was backed by the via Vittor Pisani.

The core of this irregularly shaped block was mostly made up of inaccessible airshafts, with the exception of a restaurant in an office building on the via Vittor Pisani, which used what had once been an old stable for outdoor seating in the summer months, and the Caravaggio, with its newly renovated courtyard café and private garden. Almost without exception the buildings making up the single square of masonry along the street shared a common wall, separated by nothing more than a two-foot-high course of bricks or stone to divide one roof from another.

Finn and Hilts moved across the flat, tar-papered roof, heading to the right. Reaching the end of the hotel they boosted themselves over the low barrier and stepped onto the roof of the next building. This one had a cinder-block extension for an elevator mechanical room and a few simple pipe vents, but the only trapdoor was firmly locked from the inside.

"We're going to be sitting ducks in a minute," said Hilts. "We have to find a way down. He grabbed Finn's hand and together they raced across the second roof, hopped the retaining wall to the third, and ran across it as well. Hilts guided them to an interior airshaft, but it was useless. This was Europe, and fire escapes were the exception, not the rule.

The airshaft was a black hole, picked out with squares of light from windows looking into it. Finn could just make out the litter-filled base of the shaft. Even if there had been a way down, there didn't appear to be any way out. They turned away and pelted across to the next building. This one was a full story lower than the roof they were standing on. "We'll have to jump," said Hilts. Finn just nodded.

Without pausing she dropped down to the edge of the wall, let herself over, and then let go, dropping six or seven feet to the roof of the next building. Hilts followed her, and they moved quickly across to the next low wall between the buildings. They drew up short. There was a three-foot space between the buildings. Finn looked down. For some reason the space between the buildings had been left open, and she thought she knew why. In days gone by the building's wastewater had probably run from the back of the building to the street, finally joining with whatever passed for a storm sewer in those days. The need for an open trough had gone, and the building's owners who had come after now used the space to run all manner of wiring and pipes up and down the walls, some of it modern, like the thick rubber electrical wires and the narrow phone and cable TV lines, some of it old and worn, like the lead eaves, troughs, and old-fashioned downspouts.

"We can make it," said Hilts, looking across the gap.

"Why not go down?" Finn suggested. "They're going to spot us any second."

"Maybe we can find an open hatch on the next roof," Hilts answered, looking down the narrow breach between the buildings. "And what exactly are you suggesting? It's not like there's a ladder."

"Chimney descent," said Finn. "No problem."

"What's a chimney descent?"

"Back against one wall, feet on the opposite wall, about knee-high. Put your palms on the opposite wall, thumbs down for support. Drop alternating feet, one, two, then shift your back to follow. You sort of walk down the walls, bracing yourself to keep from falling."

"You sound like you've done this kind of thing once or twice."

"Lots of times. Rock climbing was one of my hobbies at school. Climbed indoors at Lifetime and Vertical Adventure in Columbus during the winter and the real thing during the summer. It's fun."

"Sure it is," said Hilts skeptically, staring down into the cut between the buildings.

"I don't think we've got a lot of choice."

"Tell me again."

"I'll show you."

Finn sat on the edge of the gap, then slid her back slowly down, her feet braced tight against the other wall. When she was completely down she reached forward and laid her palms flat on the other wall. There was nothing holding her up now except the tension in her back and knees. She shifted her back slightly and went down a foot or two.

"This is crazy," Hilts muttered, sitting down on the wall. He dropped into the same position as Finn, holding his breath. He inched down below the level of the roofline just as the arc of a searching flashlight beam swept over the roof. "Oh godohgodohgod," he whispered, slipping down into the yawning chasm, his body held tight as a spring, sweat popping out on his forehead. He arched his back into the wall behind him and pressed his feet against the wall in front, suspended over nothingness, held up only by the strength of his desperation. Then, inch by frightening inch and foot by frightening foot, he moved himself slowly down.

21

It took less than three minutes to reach the bottom of the gap. High above they could hear shouts and running feet. Hilts dropped down into the litter in the narrow alley beside Finn and dusted himself off.

"Crazy. It worked."

"Of course it worked," Finn scoffed. "Let's get out of here before they spot us." Together they headed toward the end of the alley and the outlet to the via Locatelli.

"We've got maybe another five minutes before they close off the whole area," said Hilts, his voice low.

"Then we'd better run for it," said Finn.

"I've got a better idea." Hilts pointed toward a battered old Vespa Sprint parked a few feet away, a chain looped around the steering column and a lead pipe that ran up the side of the building beside it. He looked left and right. The narrow street was empty. More shouting came from the roof above them. He walked over to the scooter, gripped the pipe, and pulled hard. It tore away from the wall and snapped in two. He unwrapped the chain and tossed it into the alley. He checked out the scooter. "Where's the ignition?" he asked, irritated.

Finn pushed him aside and climbed onto the motor-bike. There isn't one, they only have ignition keys on the export models. I drove one of these around Florence for a whole year. Hop on."

Hilts frowned but climbed onto the rear of the narrow pommel seat. Finn took a couple of swipes at the kick-starter and the engine coughed into squeaky life. She adjusted the choke pull-down at knee level, hit the kick-stand with her heel, twisted the right hand throttle and they were off.

She turned left, away from the via Fabio Filzi and all the police cars, then left again onto via Vittor Pisani, ignoring the lights. They swept across three lanes of traffic and the central tram lane, finally turning left up the boulevard. They swung back and forth between enraged drivers, heading north toward the white grimy bulk of the Stazione Centrale, lit up like a Christmas tree half a mile ahead.

Finn turned her head slightly.

"What do I do now?" she asked.

"Head for the station."

"And then?"

"It'll take them a while to figure out we've given them the slip."

"Won't they be watching the station?"

"Probably. We'll just have to give them the slip."

"How?"

"I'll think of something, just drive."

Finn guided the Vespa north along the wide, modern boulevard, office buildings rising on either side. Hilts leaned forward in his seat and raised his voice over the racket of the old rattle-trap engine.

"We need a drugstore!"

Finn spotted the neon green cross that marked a *farmacia* on the ground floor of a building on the right. She pulled over between two parked cars and ran the Vespa up over the low curb. She put the engine in neutral but kept it running.

"What are you getting?"

"Stuff," said Hilts. "Back in a minute or two."

She waited, looking over her shoulder while Hilts ran into the brightly lit drugstore. She watched for the telltale flicker of lights and the up-and-down wail of approaching sirens, but there was nothing. It was late, but there was still a lot of traffic and the sidewalks were crowded with locals and tourists. Directly ahead was the massive, gleaming bulk of the train station. She tried to stop the terrible hammering of her heart but it was impossible. Vergadora was dead and they were looking for her and Hilts. The smart thing to do would be to put the Vespa in gear and find the nearest U.S. consulate, but she knew that the security of being on home ground was an illusion. There was physical evidence that they'd been at the old man's villa, and it was more than enough to have them turned over to the Italian authorities. They'd be trapped in the system for an eternity. Worse, if Hilts was right, Adamson's powerful friends would be able to find them wherever they were. Hilts reappeared with a plastic shopping bag. He climbed onto the back of the scooter.

"Now what?" said Finn urgently.

"We need somewhere to hide out for an hour or so."

"Movie theater?" There was a cinema two doors down from the drugstore. According to the marquee they were showing an ongoing Franco Zeffirelli retrospective. Tonight it was *Endless Love*. Somehow Finn had a hard time thinking of Brooke Shields as being part of anyone's retrospective.

"No, we need somewhere private."

"Another hotel?"

"No. Not with our faces plastered all over the news." He looked around. "You think they have such a thing as a parking garage in this town?"

"Here and there," Finn said and nodded. She spotted one of the telltale blue-and-white *P* signs on the far side of the boulevard. One of the city's bright orange trams clattered by, blocking her view for a moment, but then it was gone and she spotted the sign again. "There," she pointed.

"Get us into it," said Hilts.

In proper Italian fashion Finn ignored the traffic sign banning U-turns, bumped the scooter over the concrete lip separating the tram lane, and then swung across the far side of the boulevard between red lights and roared into the parking garage entrance. The booth attendant was gone, so Finn simply drove around the barrier arm and through the short carriageway in the base of the building fronting onto via Vittor Pisani. With parking at such a premium in the ancient city, the people who'd originally developed the office building had bought up the entire interior courtyard and built the five-story garage within it.

"We're looking for a van," Hilts instructed as they went up the ramps. Finn nodded and kept on driving. They found what they were looking for on the roof of the garage: a bright yellow Fiat Ducato light commercial van with the name Mar-cello Di Milano in red on the side. Hilts tapped Finn on the shoulder and pointed. She pulled the Vespa in beside the van and killed the engine. There were three other vehicles on the roof and they all looked like delivery vans. There were also stenciled *Riservato* notations on all the spots. Long-term reserved parking, probably for stores in the area.

"How are we supposed to get into it?"

Hilts climbed off the scooter and looked around. He found a broken, fist-sized chunk of concrete beside the waist-high retaining wall on the roof. He carried it back to the driver's-side window and slammed it through the glass.

"Like that," Hilts answered, reaching in through the broken window and opening the door.

"Very subtle." Finn got off the Vespa, put down the kickstand and climbed into the van after her companion.

"Couldn't be better," said Hilts, clicking on the dome light. The interior of the truck was filled with clothes. Racks of pants and shorts took up one side, ties and plastic-wrapped shirts were stacked on the other. Hilts knelt on the floor and spilled out his own bag of goodies: a dozen small bottles filled with some kind of muddy substance, scissors, several pairs of reading glasses, a guide-book to Milan, various small toiletries, including tooth-paste, toothbrushes, and a razor, two small cheap back-packs, and a bottle of Neutrogena Instant Bronze.

"What's all this?" said Finn.

"We can't hide your freckles and your pale skin, but we can cover it," he answered, holding up the Neutrogena bronzer. "And we can both color our hair." He checked through the pile of small plastic bottles. "You darker, me lighter." He read the labels. "Which would you like, Chocaholic or Cinnamon Stick?"

In the end she settled on Hazelnut Crunch.

Forty-five minutes later, hair towel-dried with a few of Marcello's lightweight sweaters, Finn and Hilts climbed into the front seats of the van. Finn's hair had been chopped into a boyish shag and was now a deep auburn color. The Neutrogena bronzer had darkened her face considerably, hiding the telltale redhead complexion. Hilts's hair had been trimmed as well and had gone from dirty to sun-streaked blond. Both were wearing fashionably rumpled cargo pants and brightly colored shirts, Finn's green and Hilts's bright red. A couple of clothing changes and toiletries for both of them were stuffed into the cheap backpacks. Finn and Hilts were both wearing reading glasses, Finn's large and round, Hilts's aviator style.

"This is how it's going to go," said Hilts. "Everything they expect, we won't do. They'll expect a couple, we go single. They're looking for Americans, we give them something else. What languages do you speak other than English?"

"Quite a bit of Italian, Mexican Spanish. High school French."

"How good is the French?"

"As good as high school French usually is."

"Canadian."

"What?"

"That's who you are now, a Canadian student. French, from Montreal. Your name is… What's a French-Canadian girl's name?"

"Celine Dion. Alanis Morrisette."

"Perfect. Your name is Celine Morrisette and you don't speak any Italian at all. If it gets bad, start crying and screaming in French."

"If what gets bad?"

"If they catch you."

"What about you?"

"Du er så grim at du gør blinde børn bange."

"What the hell is that?!"

"Danish for 'you're so ugly you scare blind children.'"

"I didn't know you spoke Danish."

Hilts smiled, leaned over, and kissed Finn's newly bronzed cheek.

"There's a lot you don't know about me. And I didn't mean the bit about the blind kids."

22

Finn walked through the hundred-foot-high entrance to Milan's Stazione Centrale trying to think in French, an old trick from her days writing high school exams. The trouble was, it didn't work. Instead she kept on hearing the nasal voice of her history professor at NYU telling her that the English word "crap" came from the British infantry during the Napoleonic Wars, when they couldn't pronounce the French word for "frog"—*grenouille*—so they used the Gallic word for "toad" instead, which was *crapaud,* zoologically close enough for the average English foot soldier. For some reason the story had stuck in her mind, and at that particular moment Finn couldn't think of any other word in the French language with the possible exceptions of *oui* and *non.* Trying not to panic, she made her way down the main concourse, which was roughly the size of a football field.

The interior of the station was irrationally, and wastefully, large, especially when one considered its fascist origins, a regime priding itself on ruthless efficiency. The cornerstone of the gigantic building had been laid in 1906, when Italy was still a monarchy. By 1912, the architect, a man named Stacchini, had stolen the plans for Burnham's Union Station in Washington, D.C., and had simply doubled the scale. Twenty years after that the station was finally opened, complete with a parade of goose-stepping Blackshirts marching through the same enormous archway that Finn had just walked through. The whole station, including the twenty-five platforms and the barrel-vaulted iron and glass canopies, was 1,118 feet long and covered an area of a little over 700,000 square feet. Seventy-five years after its opening the station was now home to everything from packs of meandering gypsies to several hundred professional pickpockets, twice that many home-less people, 320,000 passengers coming and going each and every day, a Gucci outlet, two McDonald's, and a Budget Rent-a-Car. It also sold railway tickets, even at midnight. Between the first McDonald's arches and the ticket counter Finn was approached by four single men of varying ages, each one attesting to his virility and his desire to buy her a drink, coffee, or a hotel room. The word "crapaud" turned out to be more useful than she'd thought. On her way to the ticket counter she also noticed at least a dozen blue-uniformed cops checking the rela-tively thin late-night crowds, each one carrying some kind of handbill. Hilts had been right: they were on the lookout for her and the photographer. She was suddenly grateful for the bad cut and dye job and the new clothes. She was also acutely aware of the fact that their passports were back at the hotel and that she didn't have a single piece of identification to corroborate her sudden incarnation as Celine Morrisette, crossover Canadian singing sensation.

"Crapaud is right," she whispered to herself, standing in the short line at the counter. Checking the big boards showing the next departures, she'd seen that there wasn't much to choose from. She reached the head of the line, tried to put on what passed for a French Canadian accent in English, and bought her ticket. Turning away from the counter she brushed past Hilts, as they'd previously arranged.

"Lyon, car eleven, compartment D, platform nine," she said under her breath, looking away from him as she passed. Hilts joined the ticket line and Finn went on ahead. The train was due to leave in ten minutes. She moved slowly, watching the entrance to the track area. There were four uniformed policemen at the gate and two plainclothes cops speaking into walkie-talkies. They weren't asking people for papers, but the plainclothesmen were eyeing the passengers as they headed through the small opening in the looming iron grille. Once again it looked as though Hilts was right, because they were paying particular attention to younger couples.

With her ticket visible in one hand Finn moved between the two policemen with their walkie-talkies, keeping her eyes forward and holding her breath. Once she was between the two men flanking the opening there would be no way to escape. She thought about how long she would last as Celine Morrisette under questioning by the police. Not long, she knew, and after all, what would be the point? If they had her, then that was that. She thought about how her mother would react back in Columbus. A simple summer job turned to crapaud. Strangely she also found herself thinking of Hilts. He was the kind of man her mother always referred to as a scoundrel, but every time she said the word it was wistful and she was smiling. Her dad, according to her mom, had been one.

"*Scusi, signorina, parla Italiano?*"

"Pardon?" She froze. She was a French Canadian named Dion. No, Celine. Crapaud.

"Parla Italiano, signorina?"

"Je ne comprends pas." That was it, the absolute bottom of the barrel. There wasn't a syllable of French left in her and her mouth had dried up like being at the dentist.

The bigger of the two men stepped forward, half blocking her path. Out of the corner of her eye she could see the sign for platform nine and the train's destination in white on black.

"Signorina, per quanto tempo sei stata di viaggio?"

The cop was asking her how long she'd been traveling. She understood every word, even in his thick, Milanese accent. But she wasn't supposed to understand him. She didn't speak any Italian because she wasn't Fiona Katherine Ryan, young art-historian-fugitive-killer-on-the-run, she was Celine Morrisette, carefree French-Canadian girl on her own, seeing Italy for twenty bucks a day and taking night trains to save on hotels.

"Signorina, per favore..."

And then, suddenly, miraculously, she had it, complete with that strange twang like a Cajun on steroids that always lurked in the back of Celine Dion's voice when she talked to Larry King. Finn let out a torrent of words, most of them to do with Raymond and his student-exchange visit and how exciting it was and all of it somehow remembered chapter, verse, and word perfect from her junior-year textbook, *Premières Années de Française*. She buried the Milanese plainclothes cop in it up to his eyeballs, all at blinding speed, along with the atrocious accent. It seemed to work. Finally Finn ran out of Raymond and his new friend Elaine's exploits, so she just shut up and smiled. The big man turned to his partner.

"Questa qua è un po' fuori," he said, which meant that Finn was a nutcase. She smiled even more. She waved her ticket.

"Canadian?" said the first cop.

She gave the cop her best revolutionary student glare. *"Non, je suis québécoise!"* She laughed, waved the ticket, and said, *"S'il vous plaît, messieurs! À ce moment je vais perdre mon train!"* It was true, the Lyon train gave a shrieking blast on its whistle. Last call.

They let her go. She made it to the train, showed her ticket to the official on the platform, and climbed aboard. The night train was one of the slower and older Corail TRNs that were being slowly replaced by the high-speed bullet-nosed TGVs, the Trains a Grande Vitesse. She found her compartment, empty at the moment, and sighed with relief. Half a minute later the whistle shrieked again, and true to Mussolini's promise, the train began to move, right on time.

Trains in Europe are almost all electric, so there was none of the North American diesel pull-and-tug as they started; the train simply began to move in a gentle, gradually accelerating motion that swept them out of the massive station and into the dark of Milan's industrial suburbs. The small compartment remained empty and Finn began to relax. It looked as though they had made it—if Hilts had managed to make it onto the train.

"This seat taken?" Hilts stepped into the compartment and slid the door closed behind him. He sat down across from her.

"You made it." She smiled.

He didn't look as happy.

"So did Badir," he answered.

"Who?"

"Badir. One of the stewards at the Adamson site. He was shadowing those two cops at the gate. He followed me onto the train."

"You're sure?"

"I've got a pretty good memory for faces. He's no steward, and he probably never was. He's muscle."

"You think he's after us?"

"I don't think he's on the train to do any damage, and I'm pretty sure he's alone. I think they put him into the station on the off chance we'd show up, and we did. He's tailing us."

"With a cell phone."

"No doubt."

"We're screwed."

"No doubt."

"So what do we do?"

"Get off the train before they can bring in reinforcements."

"Where?"

"Where the hell are we going again?"

"Lyon."

"Main line or local?"

"It's not a bullet train, it's one of the old ones, so it's probably local." She shrugged. "I'm not really sure. Does it make a difference?"

"Some. That's why I didn't want to go straight into Switzerland. They're not EU, they're neutral, so they still check your passports. Sometimes they spot-check them on the fast trains too, but if we're on a local there's less chance."

"We're going to need passports sometime."

"Let's both be Scarlett O'Hara and think about that tomorrow," Hilts suggested. "For now we have to ditch our Libyan friend Badir."

23

Finn and Hilts sat in the bar car of the humming train as it threaded itself through the alpine darkness. Finn was drinking black coffee as Hilts nursed a bottle of grape Fanta. Marco the bar-tender was fast asleep on his stool behind the U-shaped counter, arms crossed, head back and snoring. Badir, smoking endlessly and sipping from a foam cup of cold tea with lemon, was seated at the other end of the car, pretending to read an old copy of *Jours de France*. It was almost two in the morning and they were the only people in the bar car except for an old woman fast asleep over her knitting, a plastic aperitif glass vibrating gently on the round table in front of her.

"Where are we?" Hilts asked, taking a sip of Fanta and puckering at the unbelievable sweetness of the concoction. Finn had taken a sip just for fun. It tasted like liquid bubble gum.

"According to the porter putting down our bunks, we're right on the border," Finn answered quietly. "A place called Bardonecchia. We'll be going into the Frejus Tunnel in about three minutes. The tunnel is the border. We come out in France. A ski town named Modane."

"Do we stop?"

"Five minutes to switch crews."

"That's when we dump him, then."

"How?"

"You'll see."

A moment later the train slid into the tunnel and the lights flickered and died. In the darkness Hilts stood up, grabbed Finn's hand and headed back toward their sleeping car. Almost immediately they heard the sound of Badir as he clambered to his feet. Hilts pulled open the door leading into the next car and there was a sudden explosion of sound from the tracks below. Instead of moving into the adjoining car, Hilts pushed Finn into the small bathroom cubicle and eased the door shut behind them. Finn's nostrils suddenly filled with the smell of antiseptic and liquid soap. She couldn't see a thing. They heard the heavy door being pulled open a second time as Badir headed into the next sleeping car and then there was silence.

"Come on," Hilts whispered. He led Finn out of the bathroom cubicle and they stepped back into the bar car. Hilts headed back the way they'd come with Finn trailing behind. It was still almost pitch dark but there was a warning flicker from the lights overhead. "Hurry!"

They made their way into the sleeping car ahead of the bar. A passage curved to the left. Moving around the corner Finn saw that the carriage was the same as their own: passageway to the right with a line of windows, a dozen or so compartments on the left, each compartment with a varying number of bunks, from the private two-bunk room like theirs to the Cabine 8, where the narrow beds were crammed in four to each side with no more than a foot between your nose and the bottom of the bed above. They moved along the passage as the blue night-lights overhead began to flicker on again. The doors to the compartments were all closed. At the very far end of the carriage they found a Cabine 8 with the door open, which meant presumably that it was unoccupied.

"In here!" whispered the photographer.

Finn stepped into the compartment and pulled back the curtain over the lower bunk on the right. Before she could slip into it, the curtains on the bunk above slid open and a pajamaed hand clutching a very realistic-looking rabbit appeared and then spoke in English, with a dreadfully theatrical French accent.

"Bonjour, mon ami, my name is Henri. Would you like to come fishing with me?" Henri then rolled his eyes and gave a fiendishly evil laugh, like a furry Hannibal Lecter.

"What the hell is that?" said Hilts from behind her.

A face appeared behind the rabbit—a young boy with dark tousled hair, big intelligent eyes, and his other thumb stuck securely in his mouth. He took the thumb out of his mouth and poked it hard into the pale fur of the rabbit's chest. There was a brief pause and then the French accent again: "Bonjour, mon ami, my name is Henri. Would you like to come fishing with me?"

Then the boy put the rabbit down, drying his wet thumb in the armpit of his pajamas. "My name is Harry. I'm on vacation with my mother and father, who are sleeping in the next compartment, so you'd better not try anything funny. My rabbit's name is Henri. Do you like him? I do. Are we in France yet? What is France?"

Finn held her finger to her lips. "Shhhh," she whispered and smiled at the little boy. He didn't smile back.

"Why should I shhhhh? You're not my father or my mother. I don't have to do as you say." Young Harry poked

Henri in the stomach again and the bunny repeated his suggestion. Hilts leaned in over Finn's shoulder.

"I'm not your mommy or your daddy, but if you don't be quiet and go back to sleep I'm going to twist your stupid rabbit's head off and cook him up in a frying pan over a red-hot fire for breakfast, okay?"

Silently the boy and Henri retreated behind the curtain, which closed with a swish. Hilts gestured toward the lower bunk directly opposite. Finn slid into the bed and Hilts came in after her. He scrunched around so that he could look back through a crack in the curtains. They could hear a faint sniffling sound coming from the other side of the compartment.

"You didn't have to be so hard on him," whispered Finn.

"It worked, didn't it?" Hilts said. "Besides, the rabbit was a pervert." Suddenly Hilts pushed himself back onto the berth, squeezing Finn against the rear wall of the compartment. He eased the curtain completely closed. It was pitch-black in the berth. Finn could feel the hard muscles of the photographer's back against her chest and wondered if he could feel the pounding of her heart. She heard the sound of the compartment door opening. She knew if it was Harry's mother coming to check on the boy then they were doomed. There was silence for a few seconds, and then a voice.

"Bonjour, mon ami, my name is Henri. Would you like to come fishing with me?"

Finn froze, waiting, wondering if Badir was armed. There were a few whispers and then silence again. A second or two passed and then Finn heard the compartment door open and shut again. The train began to slow.

In the darkness Finn felt Hilts slip off the bunk. She followed him out into the cramped, eight-bunk compartment. Hilts opened the sliding door and peered out. In the spill of blue light Finn could see Henri staring at them from between the curtains across the aisle. Hilts turned back to Finn.

"All clear," he whispered. "Looks like we gave him the slip." He stepped out of the compartment. Finn patted Henri between the ears.

"You did good, rabbit," she said and grinned. Henri was silent. Finn followed Hilts out of the room. Ahead of her he opened the door at the end of the car and motioned her forward, and she stepped into the small area between the cars.

"He's somewhere up ahead, I think," said Hilts.

Finn nodded and Hilts threw open the door of the train car. He jumped down to the ground without letting down the short flight of metal stairs built into the car and looked left and right. Satisfied, he gestured to Finn, and she dropped down to the concrete platform. She shivered. Even in midsummer it was cold this high in the mountains. She stifled a sneeze. Ragweed. The air was full of pollen.

"I don't see him," Hilts said quietly.

Finn looked up the platform. At the head of the train she could make out a small cluster of figures. The train crews changing. There was no one else on the platform. She could see the station, a long, alpine-roofed chalet-style building with a quarried stone foundation. Behind it, a hundred yards away, was a modern building about ten stories high. A hotel perhaps. Beyond were the huge dark shapes of the Haute Maurienne, the sharp-toothed chain of mountains that marked the border between France and Italy and the southern edge of what had once been the infamous Maginot Line, the hugely expensive and utterly useless chain of defenses that was supposed to protect France from her enemies prior to the savage wake-up call that had been World War Two.

"Which way?" said Finn.

"There." Hilts pointed to the near end of the building and they ran, reaching the shadows and pausing to look up the platform again. Still no sign of Badir, or anyone else. There was a whistle shriek, then the train lurched and began to move.

"We did it," said Finn, exultant.

As she spoke a figure appeared in the open door of the sleeping carriage, crouched, and then jumped as the train began to gather speed.

"No such luck," said Hilts.

"Now what?"

"Find some transportation out of here."

They slipped around the rear of the building and found another set of tracks between them and the roadway. Finn could see a second station building and the hotel complex behind it. There was a parking lot to the right of the station with half a dozen cars. Hilts peeked around the corner of the building, then turned back to Finn.

"He's going the other way, come on."

They turned and ran, jumping off the concrete platform, slipping on the wet gravel of the roadbed, then hopping across the tracks. They reached the far platform and ducked behind it. Hilts waited for a long moment then checked to see if Badir was following.

"Still no sign of him. Maybe we got lucky."

"Don't hold your breath."

They headed to the parking lot beside the darkened station building, ducking low. Hilts went from car to car, checking through the windows. Finn chose a vantage point and kept her eyes on the tracks and the larger station building beyond, watching for Badir. There were a few tall pole lamps, but half of them had shattered bulbs and the whole platform area was in shadow. Across the road the hotel was a brightly lit beacon by comparison. She could see the sign over the door: HOTEL OLYMPIC.

She suddenly had an aromatic vision of Jack and Benny's, a greasy spoon near the campus of Ohio State University in Columbus. Breakfast. Perfectly cooked bacon and eggs, eggs over easy, bacon crisp, home fries, toast with strawberry jam and coffee. Her stomach rumbled. She couldn't remember when she'd last eaten. Somewhere on the road between the old man's villa and Milan. Hilts came back.

"What is it with this place? Every car's got an alarm. I break in we're going to wake up the entire neighborhood."

Finn heard the crunch of gravel and a voice spoke out of the darkness.

"Please keep your hands where I can see them."

She froze. A figure stepped out of the shadows. Badir, with a gun in his hand. A small, flat automatic.

"You will step back this way, out of the light."

"And if we don't?" Hilts said.

"Then I will shoot you."

"Somebody will hear the shot."

"You will be dead, however. You will not care if the sound disturbs anyone." Badir smiled.

"Why are you doing this?" Finn asked.

"Because I am paid to do it."

"By Adamson?" asked Hilts.

"This way." Badir waved the gun. "Back."

"Screw you."

A car drove into the parking lot, its lights sweeping across the three figures. Badir dropped his hand, hiding the gun at his side. He stepped back into the shadows, invisible again. Hilts and Finn stayed where they were. The car pulled in to a parking spot. The engine died, the lights went off, and a short, pudgy figure climbed out of the car. The man made a great production out of locking the vehicle, then walked toward Finn and Hilts. From a few feet away she could hear Badir's indrawn breath and she knew that the little man with the car was as good as dead. The little man continued forward, then casually lifted his arm, as though he was going to wave hello. Instead he pointed toward the shadows and a bright flash seemed to erupt from his outstretched hand, followed by a small popping noise, as though someone had exploded a damp paper bag. The first flash-bang was followed almost instantly by a second. Finn heard a sound like air going out of a tire and Badir fell forward into the light. There was a small round hole just above the bridge of his nose and his right eye was a gory mess. The pudgy little man unscrewed the suppressor from his Stechkin APS pistol and dropped the gun and silencer into the pockets of his old tweed jacket.

"Bring him round to the boot, would you?" said Arthur Simpson in a mild tone. "I'm far too old to be lugging corpses about. Plays bloody hell with my lumbago, what?" He smiled, eyes twinkling behind the thick lenses of the wire-rimmed glasses. Finn stared down at Badir. Shortsighted or not it had been amazing shooting, especially in the dark.

"I think you'd better tell us who you are first," said Hilts.

"I think you'd better think again, young fellow. Don't want to be found with the dead body of a Libyan thug at your feet, do you? The local gendarmerie would most likely have some rather awkward questions for a pair of fleeing terrorists already wanted for murder."

"His name is Simpson," said Finn. "And he's got a point."

"You know this guy?"

"We met in Cairo."

"Nice friends you've got."

"I seem to have rendered myself useful," Simpson said defensively.

Hilts gave him a long look, then bent down and picked up Badir under the armpits. Finn stepped forward and grabbed the body by the heels. They lugged him across the parking lot to Simpson's car, a nondescript nineties Mercedes 240D. Simpson opened the trunk and stepped back.

"Mind he doesn't drip on the carpets."

"Your car?" asked Hilts. He and Finn dropped Badir. Simpson closed the trunk.

"Stole it from the hotel," the white-haired man said. "Just in the nick of time apparently." He went around to the driver's side, opened the doors, and got behind the wheel. Finn got into the front seat and Hilts climbed in the back.

"How did you know we'd be here?" Hilts asked, closing his door.

"I've been following you since you left Venosa," said Simpson. He started the car, put it in reverse and turned the car around. He stopped, put the shift lever into first, then drove quietly out of the parking lot, turning left and driving right by the hotel where he'd stolen the vehicle. "I saw the fellow in the trunk shadowing you at the station in Milan and started tailing him. Thought I might be of assistance." They were out of the lights in the valley, swallowed by the night. They drove on for a few minutes, then turned off the highway onto a narrow secondary road that led up into the looming mountains.

"Where are we going, if you don't mind me asking?" Hilts queried.

"Up," said Simpson. "And back."

They drove for the next twenty minutes, the headlights of the old Mercedes revealing a narrow gravel road and a cliff on one side, a low guardrail and a dark abyss on the other. They finally reached a widening of the road like a small plateau on the mountainside, and at first Finn thought it was some kind of lookout designed for tourists.

"Now where are we?" Hilts asked sourly as they pulled off the road.

"Halfway up Les Sarrasins," replied Simpson in an excellent French accent. "A mountain."

The headlights washed over a strange, bulbous-looking structure seemingly built right into the side of the mountain. There was a dry stone wall on either side of the concrete bulge, and in the middle of that was a large steel door studded with huge rivets. The structure was clearly very old, the ancient cement dark and spawled, the façade crumbled, the doorway caked with rust.

"What's that?" Finn said.

"Technically it's referred to as *un gros ouvrage*, a large fortification. An underground fort containing roughly three hundred and fifty men. This is the main entrance. If you look closely you'll see what's left of the narrow-gauge railway tracks that used to bring ammunition and supplies up. There are several miles of tunnels and pillboxes cut into the rock. From here they could pick off anybody coming up the valley. On the backside there's a route the climbers call the Observatory. Well named. It was designed to be an early-warning outpost for an Italian invasion." Simpson shook his head. "Never happened, of course. Mussolini had many qualities but bottle wasn't one of them."

"Bottle?" said Hilts.

"Courage," answered Simpson. "What you Yanks generally refer to as balls." The potbellied man in the tweed jacket pulled the Mercedes to a halt and switched off the engine. He left the headlights on, pointing directly at the rivet-pebbled iron door.

"Why dump our friend in the trunk here?" asked Hilts.

"It's really quite difficult to dispose of a body these days," said the elderly man. He leaned across the seat and fished a flashlight out of the glove compartment, then got out of the car. Finn and Hilts climbed out after him and went around to the trunk. "Police everywhere, closed-circuit cameras, quality-control officers in the meatpacking plants. Hard to get any kind of privacy." Simpson opened the trunk and glanced down at Badir. "Your average forensic expert will have a field day with him once he's discovered. Not like the old days. Bodies floating down the Seine and up the Spree and no one really took a second look."

Together Hilts and Finn swung the body out of the car and manhandled it to the big iron door under Simpson's direction. The door was actually slightly ajar and it was easy enough to get it open. Stepping inside, Hilts swung the flashlight around. Except for the concrete floor the entire vestibule was sheathed in the same studded iron as the door, walls, ceiling, and floor. It was like being in the belly of an old battleship.

"Down the stairs," instructed Simpson, pointing with the flashlight. At the far end of the twenty-by-twenty-foot room was a massive cage elevator, like something out of a coal mine. Beside it was a circular staircase. Simpson went down first to light the way while Finn and Hilts followed with Badir, grunting under the deadweight.

"You really think he's going to be found in a place like this?" Hilts panted. "I mean, who the hell even knows this place exists?"

"Oh, good Lord! Thousands of people. Bunker freaks, military types, engineers."

"Bunker freaks?"

"Rather like people who play video games or chart the lives of serial killers on the Internet, then chat about it. Obsessive. There's a whole raft of them who make pilgrimages to old underground installations all over the world. They organize tours."

"How did you know about it?" Finn asked. "Are you, ah, a bunker freak by any chance?"

"I've been here before, actually," Simpson answered. They reached the next level. It was a long, low-ceilinged tunnel that led off left and right. Like the room upstairs, this one was sheathed in iron plate. A set of miniature railway tracks ran down the center of the concrete floor.

There was garbage everywhere, fast-food containers, beer cans, and broken bottles. Someone had made a makeshift bar in one corner and there was a rotting old mattress against the far wall. "I came here with Bernal and Solly Zuckerman before the war."

"Bernal?" said Hilts. "Solly Zuckerman?" He and Finn swung Badir onto the mattress with a thump. Finn shuddered and wiped her hands against her jeans. The iron room was cold and drafty, a fitting tomb.

"John Bernal. He was the man who started me spying at Cambridge. He was also my physics tutor. Solly Zuckerman was an expert in primate anatomy at Oxford. Strange pair."

"What were a primate anatomist from Oxford and a Cambridge physicist doing in an old bunker in France?" Finn asked.

"Blowing up monkeys to see what happened," said Simpson. He slipped on a pair of thin leather gloves and started covering Badir with a layer of rubbish. "It was 1938. They were in charge of designing air-raid shelters for the War Office. I think Bernal was talking to agents from Moscow as well. Topping the local birds as well, sly old fox he was. I was their assistant. Their young red acolyte, you might say."

"What did you do for them?" said Hilts.

"I was the one who actually blew up the monkeys," Simpson replied, tossing an old square of cardboard over the dead man's ruined face. "Set the charges and all of that. Messy business. Monkey brains all over everything." He looked down at Badir. The man was almost completely covered with litter. Simpson nodded. "He'll keep well enough. Hopefully the rats will do some damage, delay identification for a bit." The white-haired man glanced at his two companions. "Presumably you didn't think to pick up your passports when you flitted from Milan."

"No," said Hilts. "We were in a bit of a rush."

"Never mind, young fellow. I know a man down the road in Aix-les-Bains who can fix you up with new ones."

24

The first person to see Aix-les-Bains for what it was worth was probably a Roman centurion on his way into Gaul from Italy to conquer the unruly barbarians. When he mustered out of the army he returned to the pretty lakeside spot, built a pool over the hot springs, called it *Aquae Grantianae,* and a tradition was born.

Located under the shadow of Mount Revard by the shores of Lake Bourget, the largest body of fresh water in France, the little town of Aix-les-Bains has been soothing the arthritic joints of its wealthy patrons for the last two thousand years. It came into particular favor in the 1880s after a visit from Queen Victoria of England. She decided she liked it so much Her Royal Majesty attempted to buy it from the French government. They graciously declined, then built a casino and a racetrack to further fleece the charming resort's guests, renaming the hot springs Royale-les-Bains.

Special trains arrived from Paris full of high society who came to paddle on the *plage.* Steamers churned their way across the English Channel, filled with the straw hat and tennis set intent on wiling away the hot summer months in the refreshing alpine air as wives cheated on husbands, husbands on wives, and best friends on each other while Clara Butt sang "The Keys of Heaven" on the gramophone. It was *La Belle Époque* and as with all *Époques* it faded away like an old soldier, the gilt in the ceilings beginning to peel, the marble floors cracking, and the pipes carrying the hot-spring water making a terrible clanking noise and sounding much like the joints of the patrons it had once serviced. The small and ancient town hidden away in the mountains was virtually forgotten, which was exactly why Mr. Liam Alexander Pyx, the document provider, lived there; that and the town's proximity to his numbered bank accounts less than a hundred miles away in Geneva, Switzerland.

Finn Ryan awoke as the first pink rays of the sun rose over the mountains and craggy hills that marked the edge of the French Alps of the Haute Savoie. Somehow she had made her way to the backseat of the Mercedes somewhere along the way, and Hilts was now sitting in the front with Simpson, who was still behind the wheel.

"Good morning," the elderly man said brightly as she sat up, blinking and looking around. "Almost there."

"Where are we?" Finn yawned. She stared out the window. They were on a high mountain road. To the left, banks of heavy forest tilted upward; below, in the reaching light, she could see the geometric outlines of a town nestled at the far end of a long, wide lake.

"Aix-les-Bains," answered Simpson. A narrow gravel road appeared on the left and Simpson took it, guiding the old Mercedes up between the scruffy pines, the road winding around outcroppings of rock until they reached a broad, flat meadow on a small plateau. Directly ahead of them was a classic French country house right out of *Toujours Provence*: a rectangular building of old white-washed stone, a few deep windows and a steep-pitched tile roof. At the end of the lane a roughly constructed carport with a green rippled fiberglass roof sagged against the side of the house. Under it, gleaming in deep, dark blue was a very expensive two-seater Mercedes SLK230.

"Whoever this guy is he must do pretty well for himself," Hilts said, spotting the car.

"Pretty well indeed," Simpson agreed. "The war on terrorism declared by President Bush had much the same effect as Woodrow Wilson declaring war on alcohol. It's always been the same way: one way or the other, war is good for business. There's a great deal of demand for Liam's skills these days."

There was a wooden sign over the door, a name chiseled out in neat letters: LE VIEUX FOUR.

"What does that mean?"

"The Old Kiln," Simpson translated. The old man pulled the Mercedes in behind the sports car and switched off the engine, the old diesel dying with a shudder and a cough. They climbed out into the cool of the early morning. Hilts and Finn both stretched and yawned. Simpson lit a cigarette. Pyx must have had some kind of early-warning system because he was already waiting at the door, a broad smile on his friendly face. He certainly didn't look like a forger to Finn. In fact, he looked more like a rock star on vacation than anything else. He was tall, slightly stooped, wearing jeans and a white shirt with the tails hanging out. There were sandals on his bare feet. He had thick tousled, dark hair, two days' growth of beard, and behind round, slightly tinted glasses a pair of extraordinarily intelligent brown eyes. He looked to be somewhere in his late twenties or early thirties. Finn felt something stirring in the pit of her stomach and forced the feeling back where it belonged. A few hours ago she'd dumped a murdered body under a pile of rubbish, and there were police all over Italy searching for her in connection with another brutal killing. Rock star or not, this was no time for romance.

"Arthur!" Pyx said happily. "Brought me some business, have you? Or just stopping in for a pain au chocolat and a cup of my excellent coffee?" On top of the good looks he had an Irish accent like Colin Farrell.

"Business actually, but I don't think we'd turn down pastry and coffee." He turned to Finn and Hilts. "Would we?" He introduced them, one after the other, and Pyx stood aside and ushered them into his kitchen. It was relentlessly low-tech with the exception of a bright red Gaggia espresso machine making hissing, steaming noises on a simple plank countertop that looked as old as the house. The floor was dark flagstone, the ceiling plaster and exposed oak beams, the walls whitewashed stone. There was an ancient refrigerator, a freestanding pantry, a separate oven and a large, professional-looking set of gas burners. Herbs hung from nails, copper-bottom pots and cast-iron frying pans hung from the beams, and early-morning sunlight poured in through a single, multipaned window with rippled old glass set into the wall beside the grill. Outside Finn could hear birds chirping. At any other time it would have been an idyllic moment in the country; right now it was edged with fear, worry, and terror. Pyx sat them down at a yellow pine kitchen table in the middle of the room, brought out a plate of warm and aromatic chocolate croissants from the pantry, and busied himself at the exotic-looking coffeemaker for a moment, making them each a large foaming cup of cappuccino, which he then brought to the table. He sat down himself, dunked one end of a croissant into his coffee, and took a bite of the soggy pastry. Finn did the same. There was so much butter used in the flaky crust that it really did seem to melt in her mouth.

"So," said Pyx, "you don't look like the kind of people Arthur here usually brings to me, but I've learned that appearances can be deceiving."

"Passports," said Simpson. "And all the other paraphernalia."

"Talk to me," said Pyx, turning to Finn.

"What do you mean?"

"Say something—Peter Piper picked a peck of pickled peppers."

"I don't understand."

"I'm trying to see if you have an accent."

"I don't."

"Depends on your point of view. In Castleknock I wouldn't have an accent, but here I do. Speak."

Finn did as she was told.

"Columbus, Ohio," Pyx said and nodded. Finn stared.

"How did you know that?"

"Vast experience," he said, grinning. "It's what I do." Pyx turned to Hilts. "Now you," he said. "Same thing." Hilts grudgingly repeated the line of doggerel.

"Born in Florida, either Tallahassee or St. Petersburg, but you've spent a lot of time in New York, right?"

"Close enough." The photographer seemed mildly irritated that Pyx had gotten it right. If Finn hadn't known better she'd have thought Hilts was jealous, but that was ridiculous.

"Neither of you have an accent that anyone's going to be able to pick up unless they're an expert, which most U.S. passport control officers aren't. We'll make you Canadians. Either of you done much traveling there?"

"I've been to Toronto a few times, and Montreal," said Finn.

Pyx turned to Hilts. "You?"

"Same."

"Ontario then. Easy. They've got simple birth certificates and driver's license. You'll have to have a health card as well."

"Health card?"

"It's free. Ontario government. Very efficient about having the cards, and for some sort of privacy act reason they're not allowed to cross-index the databases between the bureaucracies. Good photo ID. I can do the health card, the driver's license, and the birth certificate right here."

Finn didn't understand a word of what the man was saying.

"The passports," Simpson prodded.

"Even simpler." Pyx smiled. "But first the photographs." He stood up and led the way to the rear of the house. They turned into an L-shaped hallway lined with bookcases leading to the bedroom, but instead of moving on Pyx stopped at the turn of the L and pulled out a volume from the bookcase. There was a faint clicking sound and the bookcase swung open on a completely invisible hinge.

"Open sesame," said Pyx, and stood aside to let them enter. He followed and shut the bookcase doorway behind them. Finn looked around the secret room. It was large, fifteen feet on a side and windowless. Work counters ran around three walls with built-in shelves above. There were dozens of neatly labeled binders on the shelves, color-coded, and in one corner was an array of half a dozen large flat-screen monitors. Beneath the monitors on steel racks was a row of featureless black computer servers, each one with a blinking green light on its front surface. The counters were loaded with an array of peripherals, from large flatbed scanners to photo light tables and several very professional-looking color printers and photo printers. Along the far wall was a complex three-screen Lightworks computer editing console for motion pictures.

"You're awfully free with your secrets," said Hilts. "We could have been cops."

"You're not," said Pyx. "Arthur would have killed you by now if you had been. He also let me know you were coming, and if he hadn't I would have known about it from the moment you turned off the main road." He smiled, clearly taking no offense at Hilts's comment. "And I wouldn't have greeted you with coffee and croissants, believe me." He shrugged and nodded toward the Light-works console. "Besides, I have a perfectly valid film editing enterprise going on. There's nothing here that's particularly incriminating except on the drives, and I can dump data faster than any copper could ever get into this room."

Hilts frowned. "I didn't see him call you."

"He text messaged me from Modane. I gather you had a little trouble there."

"Some." Hilts's attention was suddenly drawn to a large camera mounted on a professional tripod against the wall, facing the bookcase doorway. "That's a Cambo Wide

DS with a Schneider 35mm f/5.6 XL Digitar lens, and a Phase One P25 medium format back." His eyes widened. "That's what, thirty grand?"

"More like thirty-five," said Pyx. "Just about the most expensive point-and-shoot you can buy."

"I'd hardly call it point-and-shoot," said Hilts.

To Finn it looked like a fat lens attached to a big, flat, square piece of metal. It didn't really look like a camera at all.

"It's in line with the digitizing equipment governments use," said Pyx. "Which is how they make passports now, at least in the United States and Canada. It's supposed to be foolproof. Instead of photographs being glued and laminated, they're digitized, then thermal printed right onto the page."

"Must make your job harder," Hilts said.

"Much easier, as a matter of fact." He gestured toward the back of the bookcase door. It was painted a neutral off-white and a pair of low-level lights placed high on either side of the doorway effectively washed out any shadow. "Stand there, would you?" he asked. Hilts positioned himself against the doorway. "Head up, no smile, mouth closed," he instructed. There was a snapping sound and a bright flash and Finn realized the lights on either side of the door were photographic strobes. "Now step away and let Miss Ryan take your place." Hilts moved and Finn stood against the door. Pyx adjusted the tripod down to compensate for the difference in their heights and the strobes flared again. "Great," Pyx said and nodded. He took the flash card out of the camera, slipped it into a special drive unit beside one of the flat screens, then typed a set of instructions into the computer. "Any name preferences?"

"No," said Hilts.

"Me neither," agreed Finn.

"Okay, you'll be uh… Norman Page, and Miss Ryan will be Allison Mackenzie, how's that?"

"Whatever." Hilts shrugged.

"Fine," said Finn.

"Good Lord," Simpson said and laughed. "Do I detect a literary allusion?"

"Hardly literary," Pyx said with a smile.

"I don't get it," said Finn.

"Of course not, dear, you're far too young."

Pyx went back to the keyboard and started typing again. "Place of birth, Toronto, Ontario, Canada, date… 1981 or so, mother's maiden name… father… documents provided… guarantor." He typed on, humming under his breath, and finished the online form a few moments later. "Next thing is the routing, so it doesn't come back to me here," he explained. "First I grab an appropriate Canadian consulate… Albania, say, and put in their address as a point of origin." He read it off the screen, "Rruga, Dervish Hima, Kulla, number two, apartment twenty-two, Tirana, Albania, telephone number 355 (4) 257274/ 257275, fax number 355 (4) 257273, and finally the packet switching code." He finished typing with a flourish.

"What does all this accomplish?" Hilts asked.

"This will tell the Passport Office computer in Ottawa that Mr. Norman Page and Miss Allison Mackenzie, both presently in Paris, France, which is the closest actual passport-issuing office in the area, are renewing their passports, and have in fact already done so. It is telling the computer that the new passports are actually waiting at the embassy in Paris. Meanwhile a different set of instructions has been sent to new files along with a request for a JPEG digitization of two new passport pictures. Everything gets backdated by a few days, the passports get printed during today's run, and they'll be ready and waiting for you when you get to the embassy. Show them the birth certificates, driver's licenses, and Social Insurance Numbers I'll provide you with and they'll provide you with two perfectly authentic Canadian passports, hot off the press, orchestrated by yours truly. If one of their forensics electronic people tried to reverse-analyze the transaction, it will dead-end at the Albanian consulate, which is probably located in a dirty little hole-in-the-wall office above whatever passes for a convenience store in Tirana. It's a little convoluted, but it's a perfect hole in the system. Bust into their own database, they assume that the instructions are their own and thus legitimate and authorized. Hasn't failed me yet."

"Don't you mean Social Security Numbers?" Hilts asked.

"Don't make that mistake at the embassy in Paris if anybody happens to question you, which they won't. Social Security is American, Social Insurance is Canadian."

"But we're not going to Paris," Finn argued.

"Oh yes you are," said Arthur Simpson.

"What about Lausanne?"

"The man you're looking for doesn't live there anymore." He paused. "In fact, the man you're looking for has been dead since Thursday, September eight, 1960, at eleven twenty-two p.m."

"Awfully precise," commented Hilts dryly.

"That's when the ship went down," said Simpson. "Let's finish up with Liam and then I'll tell you all about it." Which he did.

25

With the exception of their passports they had all the documents they needed by two in the afternoon. As a bonus Pyx had thrown in two perfectly valid Bank of Nova Scotia Visa cards in their new names, each with a ten-thousand-dollar limit that, according to Pyx, would somehow be skimmed from the huge Canadian bank's vast stream of invisible wireless transfers that pinged off satellites around the world each day.

They spent most of their day at Le Vieux Four in the sun-warmed garden behind the house drinking ice-cold Sangano Blonde beer, nibbling on cheese and pate, and listening to Arthur Simpson tell his tale. As the sun warmed her Finn could almost forget why they were in this beautiful place, with its buzzing bees and chirping birds scolding them from the branches of the old birch trees at the end of the garden. Almost.

In the early afternoon, with documents in hand, they thanked Pyx for his hospitality and the speed and quality of his work, then climbed back into the Mercedes and headed down the mountain to the valley below. Finding the autoroute, they made the sixty-mile trip to Lyon in a little over an hour. Simpson dropped them off in front of the modern Part Dieu railway station.

"There are fast trains all the time. The trip to Paris takes about two hours. You should be all right. You remember the name of the hotel I told you about?"

"Hotel Normandie. Rue de la Huchette between rue de Petit Pont and the boulevard St. Michel on the Left Bank," said Finn, repeating Simpson's instructions.

"Good girl." The old man smiled.

"We owe you for the passports," said Hilts grudgingly. "I haven't forgotten, you know. We'll pay you back."

"Think nothing of it, Mr. Hilts." Simpson looked fondly up at Finn through the open window of the car. "Repaying a favor to the memory of an old friend."

"We will pay you," said Finn, her tone firm.

"On your way," Simpson ordered.

"What about you?" Hilts asked.

"I have some people to see back in Italy. But I'm sure we'll meet again before this is over. Look for me." He smiled again, rolled up the window, and drove off. Hilts and Finn turned, crossed the broad sidewalk, and went into the low-ceilinged modern terminus. They bought a pair of first-class tickets on the next high-speed train to Paris, a brand-new TGV double-decker Duplex with big airplane-style seats, lots of leg room, and a top speed of 186 miles per hour. They boarded the train, found their seats, and settled in for the relatively short journey. So far they had seen nothing suspicious, but without passports and only forged documents to identify themselves they both felt vulnerable. The train was packed, mostly with tourists of various nationalities on their way back to Paris, but they had seats together and no one paid them any attention. The train headed smoothly out of the station, right on time, and a few minutes later they were gathering speed as they raced through the suburbs of the big French city. Neither one of them had spoken since leaving Simpson at the entrance to the station.

"You want something to eat?" Hilts asked. He had taken the aisle seat, giving Finn the window.

"No, thanks."

"Drink?"

"No, I'm not thirsty," said Finn, shaking her head. "Maybe later."

"Yeah, maybe later," said Hilts awkwardly. Another moment passed.

"What do you really know about this man Simpson?" he asked finally.

"Not much," she responded. "He came to my room in Cairo. He said he knew my father. He warned me about Adamson." She paused. "He says he knew Vergadora back in the old days." She paused again. The train began to sway and vibrate slightly as they hit the open countryside and continued to gain speed. "I know he got us out of a lot of trouble last night. He's arranged for passports today. Stuff we couldn't have done ourselves."

"Like some kind of guardian angel, is that it?"

"I'm not sure."

"You ever wonder what's in it for him?"

"Yes."

"And?"

"I can't give you an answer because I don't know. I only know what he's done for us so far."

Hilts was silent for a moment. He stared at the striped fabric and the pull-down table on the seat ahead.

"You ever watch a TV show or read a book and come to a place where you stop and ask yourself, why don't they just go to the cops?"

"Sure," Finn said. "It's like in a horror movie when the girl goes down into the dark basement and everybody but her knows she should turn and run."

"But if she did, the movie would end right there," agreed Hilts. "That's where we are. We're at the place where the movie should just end, because if we had any brains we'd run to the cops."

"But we can't. They want us for killing Vergadora."

"And our guardian angel, your friend Mr. Simpson, who keeps on turning up, is helping us to get away from the cops."

"What are you getting at?"

"He's keeping the movie going."

"So?"

"Why?" Hilts asked. "Unless he wants us to keep on looking for DeVaux." He paused. "Or unless we're being led into some kind of trap."

"That thought had crossed my mind," Finn said abjectly. "But what are we supposed to do about it now?"

"That story he told us today, out in Liam Pyx's garden, about DeVaux."

"What about it?"

"Do you believe it?"

"I don't know. I'm still trying to figure that out."

26

While they'd waited for Pyx to create their new identities, Simpson had told them about his relationship with the vanished monk and with the man who'd been after him for years, Abramo Vergadora. According to Simpson, Hilts was correct; not only was Vergadora now a *sayan* for Israeli Intelligence—the Mossad—he had once been an active member, back before it, or Israel itself, had even existed. In the late thirties Simpson had met the Italian Jew at Cambridge, where Vergadora was reading anthropology and archaeology under Louis Clarke and T. C. Lethbridge, who was curator of Anglo-Saxon Antiquities at the Cambridge Archaeological Museum. With the war Vergadora chose to join British Intelligence in Switzerland rather than return to Italy and face persecutions under Mussolini. He eventually joined the so-called Jewish Brigade, which infiltrated German-speaking Jews into Germany toward the end of the war as resistance fighters and spies. Through his work he discovered DeVaux's history with his own archenemy Pedrazzi, and also learned that after Pedrazzi's disappearance in the Libyan Desert, DeVaux had briefly reappeared in Venosa to dig in the old catacombs, and then fled again, this time to America. Somewhere along the line, perhaps with the help of old friends at the Vatican, he managed to change his name to Peter Devereaux and resurfaced as an assistant curator at the Wilcox Classical Museum at the University of Kansas in Lawrence.

"Pretty obscure," Hilts had commented.

"Obscure perhaps, but fitting," replied Simpson, nibbling on a small piece of baguette slathered with fresh churned butter and goose liver pate. "The Wilcox is entirely given over to Greek and Roman antiquities, including one of the world's best collections of Roman coins and medallions. Just like the one you found on Pedrazzi."

DeVaux-Devereaux had kept a low profile at the university for years, but according to Vergadora he had continued his researches and also his connections with the school in Jerusalem. According to Vergadora, and confirmed by Simpson, the school was more than simply an institute for biblical archaeology; it was also a Vatican listening post in a chronically troubled part of the world and always had been.

According to information gathered covertly by his friends in the Mossad, Vergadora found out where DeVaux had been hiding and what his new identity was. Following this information, at least according to Simpson's story, Vergadora also found out that the onetime Vatican archaeologist had made a discovery of profound religious and historical significance: the so-called Lucifer Gospels, written by Christ himself—after the Crucifix-ion. The gospels, sometimes also known as Christ's Confession, told the story of how Christ's place was taken by his brother James in the Garden of Gethsemane and then "betrayed" by Judas to the Roman soldiers who came to arrest him, the soldiers having no idea of what Christ looked like. Christ, with the help of several recently converted Romans, was spirited away into the wilds of the Libyan Desert, where he lived a long life as a hermetic monk. His own mythology eventually became confused with that of the Lost Legions, Zerzura, and his so-called Aryan protectors, the blue-eyed fair-haired Knights of Saint Sebastian. All of this, of course, completely denied the entire foundation of the Catholic Church and of Christianity as a whole; a disaster of monumental proportions when even the most basic tenets of the Church were under attack. Even more bizarrely, it seemed that DeVaux-Devereaux had made this discovery in the United States. By his estimation the gospels had been transported by early Templar explorers deep into the central United States, perhaps along with the greatest treasure of all: the bones of Jesus Christ himself. Myth or reality, either way it was a story with powerful implications for everyone.

DeVaux-Devereaux's discovery eventually led to an agreement to meet, but on neutral ground. The onetime Vatican historian knew that his information, and his proof, were inherently both incredibly valuable and equally dangerous. The meeting was to take place in Nassau in the Bahamas, easy enough for both parties to reach, on board the French passenger liner the *Île de France,* now renamed the *Acosta Star.* The man he was to meet with was a scholar named Bishop Augustus Principe from the Pontifical Institute of Biblical Studies in Rome. Unfortunately, soon after leaving the Bahamas, with DeVaux-Devereaux on board, the ship caught fire and sank. In the process the ex-priest and Bishop Principe were killed and the secret of the Lucifer Gospel lost. First Vergadora and then Simpson had managed to check the bare facts of the story and found them to be true: there had been a spate of three-way coded correspondence between the school in Jerusalem, the Vatican secretariat, and the man known as Peter Devereaux in Lawrence, Kansas, and the *Acosta Star* had in fact sunk somewhere in the Caribbean on Thursday, September 8, 1960, at 11:22 p.m. with a man named Peter Devereaux listed on the passenger manifest.

And that was that. The story that had begun in the hot sands of the Libyan Desert had its final chapter in the blue-green waters of the Caribbean, a journey of two thousand years and twice that many miles. A journey, like many involving the word and deeds of many gods, that had been drenched in the blood of the innocent and guilty alike.

The rest of the trip from Lyon to Paris was completely uneventful. The train pulled in to the Gare de Lyon exactly on time and a well-mannered Parisian taxi driver took them across the city to the Petit Pont, crossed Île de la Cité to the Left Bank and deposited them in front of the five-story Hotel Normandie on the rue de la Huchette, a narrow, forgotten backwater off the Place St. Michel that looked as though it hadn't changed much since Napoleon's time, or at the very least since German soldiers wandered down its one long block looking for local color on furlough in the City of Light. There were butchers, bakers, a tobacconist, two other hotels of the same pension class as the Normandie, a place that sold orthopedic supplies, and an assortment of other small businesses of the kind found in any other neighborhood. The Café St. Michel on the corner fed them a decent meal and a bottle of *vin ordinaire,* and then they went to their separate beds, exhausted. The following morning, after they consulted first a telephone directory and then a map, they discovered that the Canadian embassy on avenue Montaigne was within reasonable walking distance. They set out in the bright morning sunlight, crossing the Seine at le pont des Invalides, then heading up toward the Champs-Elysées and the upper end of the diplomatic district off the avenue Foch. The embassy turned out to be a discreet assembly of three Napoleon III buildings on a pleasant, tree-lined street and without a red-coated Mountie in sight. With some trepidation Finn and Hilts ventured inside. The interior had obviously seen some anti-Osama renovations, but in the end the whole process was a completely predictable affair of plastic chairs, number taking, and polite lines in bank lobby zigzags. An hour after entering the embassy they exited, the possessors of two blue-and-gold Canadian passports.

"Well, that was easy," said Hilts, relieved. They turned down avenue Montaigne, heading back to the hotel.

The takedown was professional, perfectly executed, and went without a hitch. There was a man in front, dressed casually in jeans and a dark blue sweatshirt, with a rottweiler on a leash, and two men behind, armed. A green Mercedes pulled up on the left, the rear door swinging open. One of the two men behind stepped forward, nudging something hard into the small of Finn's back, urging her into the car, the second man doing the same to Hilts, while the man with the rottweiler stood by, blocking the possibility of an intrusion from people on the sidewalk, the dog growling low in the back of its throat. One of the men behind climbed in after Finn and Hilts, the second slammed the door, and the car began to move. It had all taken less than twenty seconds. Finn managed to look out through the rear window. The man with the dog was moving off as though nothing at all had happened, and the second man went off in the opposite direction.

Finn and Hilts were crushed together in the rear seat, a man on either side of them. A third man sat in the front seat beside the heavyset driver. The man beside the driver turned. His hair was dark and very short. He had a full beard and was wearing tinted glasses, and had a small leather folder in his hand with an ID card showing the famous sword-through-the-world-with-the-scales-of-justice logo of Interpol on it. He showed it first to Hilts and then to Finn without a word, glared at them, then snapped the folder shut and turned in his seat, facing forward.

Finn folded her hands in her lap, heart pounding. Beside her Hilts folded his arms across his chest and glared at the space between the driver and his companion. Finn had only been in Paris once before, and then only for a few days. The scenery blowing past meant nothing; broad avenues, statues, trees, long façades of buildings that all seemed to date from roughly the same Empire period of architecture. A sense of grandeur and grime, of packed, wide sidewalks and chaotic traffic. The Mercedes stopped and started, the driver swearing and blowing his horn along with the rest of them. But the driver wasn't swearing in French; it was some dialect of Arabic full of spitting gutturals. A barked word from the man beside the driver shut him up.

"Said bousak, Hmar!"

They sped through a traffic circle and Finn saw that they were going up a wide boulevard, an outdoor market set up with dozens of stalls and vendors laid out on the broad, tree-lined sidewalk to their right. They swerved to avoid a car on their left and Hilts slammed against the man beside him. The man gasped and flinched, his face twisting in agony as he lurched against the door. Hilts pushed harder and the door swung open, the photographer's thrusting shoulder heaving the screaming man hurtling out of the car and into traffic. From behind them came a horrible thumping sound and the screeching of brakes, but almost before anyone could react Hilts's right hand moved in a blur and four inches of wavy-bladed steel was suddenly jutting from the base of the driver's neck. He shrieked, both hands flying up from the wheel to flail at the black-handled instrument sticking out of his neck. The car swerved, jolted wildly, and then hit something hard. The car came to a rocking halt. Grabbing Finn's hand, Hilts threw himself out of the car and into a pile of cabbage.

"Come on!" he yelled. They climbed to their feet and staggered away from the wreckage of the car. The man beside the driver was struggling with his air bag. The driver had pulled the blade out of his neck and was desperately trying to stem the squirting fountain of blood with his bare hand.

Together Finn and Hilts ran through the market, slamming into shoppers and sending string bags full of groceries flying in all directions. Tradesmen swore as they raced on, and they felt hands reaching out to grab at them. Finn could hear a police whistle and in the distance a siren.

Suddenly the flat, cracking sound of an automatic pistol tore through the air. The man from the car was firing at them. The people around them in the market began to panic, dropping to the ground or scurrying away, yelling and screaming. There was a hot breeze half an inch from Finn's cheek, and then came the sound of the gun again.

"The Métro!" Hilts yelled, dragging her to one side. They were at the end of the line of market stalls. The last one was butted up against the rail of the opening that led down into the subway. Hilts vaulted over the railing and Finn followed him, landing on her feet, almost toppling down the stairs, terrifying a woman and her poodle as they came out of the tunnel. Limping after the long drop, they hobbled down the white-tiled tunnel, fumbled with change to buy a *carnet* of tickets at a machine, and stumbled through the big pneumatic doors just as a train rattled into the station. They waited until the train came to a stop, then pushed their way on as soon as the doors hissed open. They sat down, chests heaving, and Finn saw their pursuer squeezing himself illegally through the rubber bumpers of the pneumatic doors at the platform entrance. The horn sounded and the man was forced to step onto a car six or seven down from the one they were sitting in.

"He got on," she whispered to Hilts.

"I saw," he answered.

"What do we do?"

"I'm thinking."

"Think faster."

The train banged through the station then headed into the intersecting tunnels that cut beneath the city. The wheels screeched as they rounded each turn, the cars rocking and heaving. They were on the first and oldest of the subway lines in Paris, Number One, and it felt like it.

"He'll move ahead each time we stop, maybe a couple of cars each time. That gives us three stops before he's on top of us."

"Where's that?"

"Where did we get on?"

"Some place called St.-Mandé de something or other."

"Where does that leave us?"

Finn checked the map over the door.

"Reuilly-Diderot."

"Is it a main stop, a what do you call it, a correspondence stop?"

"No."

"What's the next one of those?"

"Nation," she answered. "Two stops."

"Be ready to get off there. We have to lose him."

"Where did that knife come from?"

"Your friend Simpson gave it to me in the car when you were asleep. Nasty little thing, a front-loading switchblade, state of the art. Made in Italy. He said he had two."

"Who were they?"

"Not Interpol, that's for sure. The guy was speaking Arabic and the other guy swore at him."

"I heard."

They came into the next station—Porte de Vincennes. A few people trickled on and off. The horn sounded and the train moved off again.

"Head for the doors," said Hilts. They got to their feet and stood in front of the right-hand doors.

"*L'autre côté,*" instructed an old man in a raincoat and a dark blue beret. He was smoking a hand-rolled cigarette directly under a sign stenciled on the window that read DEFENSE DE FUMER.

"What?" said Hilts.

"Other side," Finn translated. "I know that much French. I think he means the platform is on the other side." She smiled at the old man. "Merci," she said.

"Parle a mon cul, ma tête est malade," the old man answered, making a sour face.

"What did he say?" asked Hilts.

"Nothing very nice, I don't think," Finn answered. The train thundered into the station. It was much more modern than the previous ones and had half a dozen different tunnel exits. They chose the closest, cutting through the throng of arrivals and departures.

–

"Where are we going?"

Finn checked the line. "Étoile."

"What's that?"

"The Arc de Triomphe."

"Where we started."

"Approximately."

Hilts looked back over Finn's shoulder, searching the crowd spilling out onto the platform.

"See him?"

"Not yet."

The horn sounded as a train came into the station. Behind them the pneumatic doors began to close. The train screeched to a halt and the doors of the cars slid open. Hundreds of people swarmed past them.

"There!" Finn spotted the man with the beard and the tinted glasses pushing his way onto the platform. Someone yelled at him, cursing, but he ignored it. Hilts grabbed Finn by the elbow and thrust her forward into the nearest car. He followed, watching over his shoulder. The doors slid closed, leaving the bearded man on the platform. As the train pulled out, leaving him behind, Hilts saw him lift a cell phone to his ear.

"He's making a call. Bringing up reinforcements. Shit!"

"We can't stay on the train for very long," said Finn. "He could have people waiting for us ahead." She looked up at the map above the doors. If the man with the beard was quick enough and smart enough he'd realize that he could even get ahead of them by going one more stop on the Number One line—Bastille—then double back on them using the secondary Number Five line that ran between Bastille and the southern stations. The Paris Métro was incredibly complex, and after more than a hundred years of development there wasn't a building in the city that wasn't within five hundred yards of a subway stop.

At the very least there would be someone waiting for them at Montparnasse-Bienvenüe, the next big corresponding stop, with half a dozen lines crossing each other. They pulled into the station at Place d'Italie and then moved out again. At least he hadn't been quick enough to get someone in place there. According to the map they had only two chances before the next big stop. It was going to be either Denfert-Rochereau or Raspail. She didn't know anything about either place, but both were close to Montparnasse, once the center of bohemian life in Paris, but now not much more than a slightly down-at-the-heels tourist area full of cafés advertising themselves as Lenin's Favorite Restaurant or Hemingway's Bar.

"Next stop then," Hilts said. Once again they moved toward the doors. The train slowed then came to a squealing halt. They got out of the car and headed down the crowded platform. As the train pulled out Finn glanced across to the opposite side of the tracks and saw the startled look of a man on the other side—the same man who had pushed Finn and Hilts into the car outside the Canadian embassy. He stared for a moment, open-mouthed, then sprinted for the exit.

"They're on to us!"

Finn and Hilts ran to the nearest exit, then climbed up the long flight of stairs, ignoring the parallel escalators. They reached the upper lobby and crossed it, rushing out of the big station. They pushed through one of the three arched entrance doors, breathing hard. Without stopping they ran out into the street, dodging traffic, and made it to the circular plaza in the center, mounted with a huge bronze statue of yet another man on a horse. Once upon a time Paris must have been a wonderful place to own a foundry, Finn thought.

"Which way?" she said.

"Doesn't matter. We have to lose him. Run!"

He took her hand and pelted into the street. A car screeched to a halt next to a taxi stand. A Mercedes, this one blue. The man with the rottweiler jumped out, minus the dog. Behind them the man on the platform was dodging through traffic, crossing the street toward them. They swerved, reaching the sidewalk, and ran headlong up a short flight of steps and through a pair of tall black doors, open against the summer heat.

A man in a uniform sat on a stool beside a turnstile set up in the middle of a large, dark, marble-floored room.

He looked bored. A sign on the turnstile read: E10. Ten euros. Hilts jammed his hand into his pocket, pulled out a few crumpled notes and shoved them into the attendant's hand. They rushed through the turnstile, and Finn looked back over her shoulder to see if the men were following. So far there was no sign of them. She turned again. In front of them was nothing but the circular entrance to a staircase in the floor.

"What is this place?" Hilts asked, staring at the dark spiral of stairs at his feet. "Is this some kind of sewer tour?"

Finn knew. She'd read about it in a guidebook the last time she was in Paris. Not the sewers.

This was the entrance to the Paris Catacombs, home to the dead of centuries, millions of them, hidden deep beneath the streets of the old city.

27

As a city Paris has been in existence for more than two thousand years. It began as a small village on the Île de Paris, where Nôtre Dame Cathedral now stands, then spread out on both sides of the Seine, north, south, east, and west. Like any rapidly expanding urban center, Paris had two major problems, both of which caused terrible and sometimes fatal health problems: garbage and dead bodies. Both brought disease on their ragged coattails. By the Middle Ages the garbage crisis caught up with Paris in the form of the Black Death—bubonic plague. A little while later the dead bodies caught up with Napoleon as he tried to create his vision of the city and kept tripping over putrid corpses in overflowing cemeteries from one side of Paris to the other. For a millennium or more the thousand or so churches in the city had each maintained its own cemetery, but as Napoleon renovated, the graveyards kept on getting in the way of his version of town planning. Paris, like Washington, D.C., after it—both designed by the same man, Pierre L'Enfant—was built on a swamp. Bodies weren't so much buried as floated in a sea of muck. Napoleon, dictator, emperor, and practical man that he was, decided that every cemetery was to be emptied and the remains transferred to the old Roman limestone workings on what was then the edge of the city. As the redevelopment of the city continued the plan was put into effect. The newly dead were interred in three main burial grounds, Père Lachaise, the best known, which holds the remains of famous people as diverse as Jim Morrison of the Doors and Frederic Chopin, while the other two, Montparnasse and Montmartre, got the leftovers. The bones of seven million others were gathered up and taken to the limestone quarries to be hidden away two hundred feet below the surface. Over time, limestone quarries and boneyards combined covered more than a hundred and fifty miles of galleries on both sides of the Seine, with secret exits and entrances through sewers, manholes, and old buildings across half the city. The Nazis used some of them as communications bunkers and air raid shelters. At the same time, the Paris Resistance used other sections of the same network for meetings and to store weapons. According to history, the two factions never once ran into each other. The one squad of SS sent down to rout out the freedom fighters vanished without a trace.

Finn and Hilts headed down the stairway. The temperature began to drop almost immediately, the summer heat turning to a clammy, naturally air-conditioned coolness that made Finn shiver. They kept on moving down the narrow, shallow steps, deeper and deeper. Small bulbs hanging from a frayed cable wrapped around the stone core of the staircase lit their way. Finn began to count the steps to take her mind off the steadily increasing sense of claustrophobia. They hit bottom at 234. She could hear footsteps echoing behind them but she had no idea if it was their pursuers or just a bunch of tourists who'd paid their ten euros. A marker on the wall informed them that they were seventy meters below ground—230 feet. A line of dim bulbs ran away into the distance. There was no other way to go except back up the stairs and into the clutches of the men chasing after them. The floor beneath their feet crunched wetly. Damp gravel. The walls and ceiling of the stone-lined tunnel were dripping. *A hell of a place to die,* Finn thought.

A hundred yards farther on the tunnel began to widen and she felt her claustrophobia lessen slightly. Suddenly the tunnel emptied out into a broad and well-lit vestibule. The ceiling, sweating coldly, was still no more than a yard above their heads. The vestibule was oblong, with a pair of Egyptian-style obelisks carved into the rock on either side of a gaping doorway. The obelisks were white with rectangular inserts of black. Above the doorway, carved into the stone, was a message and a warning, written in Latin. Finn translated the words aloud:

"Stop! You are about to enter the Empire of the Dead."

"Lovely," muttered Hilts. They stepped between the obelisks and went through the dark doorway into a vision from the depths of a cave-cool hell.

Stretching away in all directions, lit only by the pale clear bulbs that hung from the ceiling, stacked like cord-wood and piled head-high in ornate rows twenty feet thick, were piles of human bones. Yellow, damp, old— it was layer upon layer of thighbones, pelvic bones, arms, legs, collar-bones and spinal vertebra, tens of thousands of skulls, eye sockets leering blindly jaws and teeth locked together into perpetual smiles by the dripping lime from above, all sense of humanity fled like the inner workings of a mass murderer's most passionate dreams of bony carnage, an enormous mass of bone that was slowly, as secretions fell, becoming a single, monumental and monstrous fossil.

The damp air was filled with a sweet-sick musty odor of old age, and the only sound was the muffled whispers of their rasping breaths.

"My God," said Finn, awe-stricken. She took Hilts's hand and squeezed it hard.

"There's probably other people up ahead. Come on," he said. Together they moved down the corridor of bones, peering ahead through the deadly gloom. Every fifty feet or so along the loose-floored passage they could see side tunnels blocked by wrought-iron barriers. It was clear that major sections had been blocked off to keep people from wandering through the entire place, becoming lost forever. They passed a wheelbarrow with a shovel laid across a load of assorted bones; clearly the gigantic ossuary was still in use.

Hilts stopped. "Wait," he said. He turned and listened. At first there was only silence, and then they both heard it: a soft, rodentlike scuffle, like rats on a barn floor. Running feet on gravel. "They're coming!" He looked around wildly, then picked up the shovel on the wheelbarrow. He hefted it. No match for a gun, that was sure enough. Finn spotted a side passage on the opposite side of the main corridor. The wrought-iron gate was hanging off its simple hinge.

"In there!" she said. Hilts nodded. They moved across to the other side of the passage and squeezed through the opening. The sounds of their pursuers were getting dangerously close. Hilts turned and lifted the narrow gate, dropping the rusty pins back into their sockets with a loud scraping sound that made him wince.

"No!" Finn exclaimed with a groan.

"What?"

"Look!" She pointed through the grating. There on the floor of the tunnel, ten feet away, was a brand-new passport, the gold-stamped Canadian crest gleaming proudly in the sullen light from the dim bulbs overhead.

"Which one is it?" Hilts said. Finn reached into the pocket of her jacket and pulled out the passport she'd picked up no more than an hour before.

"Idiot!" groaned Hilts, chiding himself.

"What do we do?" asked Finn.

"Hope they don't notice," said Hilts. He pulled Finn back into the shadows. The sound of footsteps was very clear now. Finn was suddenly aware of the impenetrable darkness behind them, and her imagination was more than capable of visualizing what that ghastly blackness held. Miles of corridors, millions of skulls, twice as many sightless eyes staring into eternity.

The footsteps slowed. Finn saw shadows cast off their pursuer by the thin light overhead. The footsteps stopped dead. One person. He'd seen the passport and was trying to figure out what it meant. The figure stepped forward into his own shadow. It was the bearded man from the car; he'd managed to switch back and meet with his companion from the opposite platform at Denfert-Rochereau. He had a gun in his hand, a very modern-looking automatic made from some sort of flat black composite polymer. There was a fat sausage-shaped thing attached to the barrel. A silencer, she guessed. He wasn't going to draw any attention to himself. As he bent to pick up the passport, the gate pin settled into its socket with a small clanking sound and the moldy old bones finally proved too much for Hilts. He sneezed.

The man whirled, gun arm extended. A cold green light leapt out from the top of the weapon like a sinister ghoulish thread—not only a silencer, but a laser sight. Finn felt Hilts's hand on her shoulder, pulling her back even farther into the darkness. She held her breath and stepped back as quietly as possible. She reached up with one free hand to guide herself back through the dark, her fingers trailing over the stacks of bones. The bearded man shoved the passport into his jacket pocket, then stepped up to the gate and started manhandling it out of its sockets. Hilts's hand squeezed her shoulder again, and silently she kept moving back. Her free hand suddenly reached out and touched empty air. Hilts guided her around into a second side passage, this one running away at a right angle from the first. Finn's fingers touched a skull in the wall to her left. She slid her fingers into the eye sockets, hooking them around the nasal sinus. She eased the skull from its place in the wall. It slid into her hand with a faint wet scraping sound. She gritted her teeth and hefted the skull. About two and a half pounds. It suddenly occurred to her that she was ahead of Hilts. If the bearded man turned and fired she'd be the one to get shot. She froze. Directly ahead of her she could see the line of green light from the laser sight. She felt her muscles tightening. If he continued along the side passage there was a chance they could get in behind him and escape. She held her breath again, listening for the sounds of the man's footsteps. Instead she heard a small scurrying noise behind her and then a squeak. Hilts swore and the line of green light turned down the second side passage and blazed into Finn's eyes. She didn't even pause to think. She took one step forward, totally blinded, and straight-armed the skull at a point two feet above the searching beam of the laser, holding the bulbous cranium like a boxing glove on the end of her hand. There was a hard cracking sound as the skull connected, then fell apart on her fist. She heard a sighing hiss like air going out of a tire and the laser light wavered, then spun down as the bearded man dropped to the floor of the passage. The beam illuminated the mess Finn had made of his face. He was unconscious, his nose broken and his lip gashed. The left side of his chin also seemed a little out of place.

"Glass jaw," commented Hilts. He bent down and retrieved his passport from the man's pocket. He picked up the gun, slid out the clip, then threw the weapon into the deeper darkness behind him.

"Strong left jab," answered Finn. She picked up the two bloody pieces of the skull and examined them.

"I wonder who you hit him with?" said Hilts.

"We'll never know," she replied. She gently placed the two pieces of the skull back on the stack of bones.

"Let's get the hell out of here," said Hilts.

They made their way back to the main corridor and ran down it. Ten minutes later they reached another portal and the passageway began to slope upward, the walls bare limestone now instead of bones. Another ten minutes brought them to a second spiral staircase, where a woman sat behind a desk selling postcards and slide sets and a second uniformed guard sat with a sour expression on his face. Finn and Hilts climbed the long flight of stone steps and reached a small, plaster-walled room with a single push-bar door. They pushed and stepped out into blinding sunlight. Finn felt a swift wash of relief, as though she'd been granted a reprieve.

"He'll be coming to by now if he hasn't already," Hilts warned. Squinting, Finn looked at their surroundings. They were on an unnamed backstreet somewhere. The wall behind them was whitewashed stone covered with peeling old graffiti. The tag on the wall read "Bad Idea." Finn couldn't have agreed more.

"Where to? she asked.

"Well, thanks to you we both have passports again, so maybe we should use them," offered Hilts. "I'm beginning to think we've worn out our welcome in Europe."

"Simpson said DeVaux's last port of call was Nassau."

"I can't think of a nicer hideout. The Bahamas it is."

28

In any other country Nassau International Airport would have been a bus station. Low ceilings, fake wood paneling on the walls, cracked floor tiles, and cheap yellow plastic seats in the waiting room. Sometimes, if the Tourist Office is in the mood, a grouchy steel band will be banging away in one corner surrounded by cardboard cut-out palm trees and homemade Christmas tinsel.

U.S. customs preclearance for people on the way out means that lines sometimes trail outside the building and into the parking lot. Most of the time neither the air conditioning nor the conveyor belt work. The airport personnel don't work at all unless they have to. The security checks are about as lax as the ones you get at Ouagadougou Airport in Burkina Faso. There is only one set of toilets and one cafeteria-style restaurant, and only one shop, called Nature's Gift, which sells only soap. This is the place where people from the United States come to catch a flight to Havana. Once this was the gateway to Paradise.

This Eden, however, like any other, was prone to corruption. The snake in this garden was organized crime, and the apple from the tree of knowledge looked suspiciously like cocaine and marijuana going in one direction and bales of hundred-dollar bills going in the other, after spinning around in electronic Laundromats with names that sounded like banks but weren't. One way or the other six hundred and fifty metric tons of cocaine and ten times that much marijuana flowed through the islands of the Bahamas every year. The cash would fill a hundred freight cars. Cockroaches in the Bahamas have wings, lizards are everywhere, and the roads are full of potholes. When the Disney cruise ships dock in Nassau they play the first four bars of "When You Wish Upon a Star" on their horns so loudly you can hear it on the other side of New Providence Island.

On the other hand, the sand is blindingly white, the sea is the color of emeralds, and the sky is like sapphires. Swimming is like paddling around in a giant hot tub full of tropical fish. The people are polite and genuinely friendly, it rains for an hour or so every day just when you're getting a little too hot, and they don't put white people in jail, if the Fox Hill Penitentiary is any indication. Public transportation is cheap, fun, and frequent and the food is wonderful.

Finn and Hilts managed to catch a shuttle from Paris to London and then a nonstop flight from there to New Providence. Thirteen hours and ten minutes after climbing out of the Paris Catacombs they were climbing into a cab at the airport in Nassau. The sun beat down like a hammer, and the cab was without air conditioning. Swain & the Citations were doing "Duke of Earl" on the stereo.

The driver introduced himself as Sidney Poitier. He looked just about the right age for it, his eyebrows and the stubble on his chin stark white against his dark skin. He was wearing round, tortoiseshell glasses that looked old enough to really be made from tortoiseshell. The eyes behind the lenses were watery with age and desperate experience beyond imagining. They were also bright with humor and intelligence. Uncle Remus driving a taxi. What Richard Pryor might have been like at seventy, Finn thought.

"Is that really your name or just something for the tourists?" Hilts asked, surprised.

"My name before his. I believe I'm a year or two older. Poitier's nothing special on the islands for a name. Sidney neither. He from Cat Island, as I recall. My old dead mother say he was a bad one so they send him to Miami to get good. That a laugh, General: the word 'good' and the word 'Miami' like oil and water; no mixing them up. I say to people, my name's Sidney Poitier, and they say, Guess who's comin' to dinner, but it sure as shit ain't this Sidney eatin' at the Royal Bahamian in the damn heat of the night. Which say, you goin' anyplace in particular or you just want me to drive you around, General?"

"A hotel," said Finn. She'd slept well enough on the long flight but she definitely needed a shower.

"You come from England on the B.A. and you don't have a reservation?" Sidney asked.

"We were pressed for time," said Hilts. The only luggage they had were a pair of British Airways flight bags they'd picked up at Heathrow and filled with necessaries from the airport shops.

"You eloping or something like that, General?" asked Poitier. The taxi was sweeping around the forested edge of Lake Killarney. Pine trees, not palms.

"Something like that."

"Then you lookin' for something you might call more or less secluded, right?"

"More or less," Hilts agreed.

"Got just the place for you then, General," said Poitier, agreeably.

"I thought you might."

They turned off John F. Kennedy Drive onto the scruffy track of old Blake Road and soon came out onto West Bay Street and the chain of condo complexes, gated communities, and million-dollar beachfront bungalows that make up Sandyport.

Following Bay Street along the coast they reached Cable Beach, with its long row of high-rise hotels, night-clubs, and restaurants. Eventually the hotels faded away as they went around the deep, pretty curve of Go Slow Bend and reached the narrow strip of public park at Saunders Beach. After that the bloom was off the rose. A mile out in the water a white concrete tower that looked like something out of *The Jetsons* ruined the view, and Poitier told them it was the old Crystal Cay Observation Tower and Aquarium and was usually closed for one reason or another.

On shore the beachfront houses became older and crummier, interspersed with bars, clubs, and condo units poking up through the sand and limestone and sparse patches of grass. Just past a yellow house, surrounded by a razor-wire-topped stone wall, the taxi turned again and they pulled up into the driveway of a time-battered Victorian clapboard with a screened porch and narrow windows that looked as though it belonged on the set of *Psycho*. A carved wood sign out front announced that this was the office of Sir Percival Terco, M.P., Minister of

Justice. Directly across from the big old house was a row of fish-fry shacks. The nearest one said Deep Creek.

Poitier grunted. "Percy hasn't been Minister of Justice since Linden O. Pindling in ninety-two, but he likes the sign. And nobody here calls him Sir, believe me, General. He went away to England on holiday a few years back, came home and said Queen Elizabeth knighted him while he was there. Brought back a fancy piece of parchment with the Terco crest on it. Said it was hundreds of years old. Swans on it." He snorted. "Black swans, maybe." The old taxi driver laughed. "Motel's around back."

He drove in behind the house. A long L-shaped white building that looked like renovated slave quarters or a transformed chicken house stood at the end of an asphalt lot. There seemed to be seven units. There was a strange cupola like an afterthought on top of the building and a set of stairs running down to the ground with a banister made of old pipe. In the middle of the parking lot was a raised wooden platform in the shape of a boat. Above it was a sheet of rippled fiberglass, just like the one over the carport of Pyx's place in Aix-les-Bains, except this one was yellow instead of green and topped in turn by a big satellite dish. There was a television mounted in a padlocked wooden box in what would have been the bow, a Ping-Pong table amidships, and a charcoal barbeque in the stern. Where the rudder would have been on a real ship was a public telephone mounted on a pole. In between the barbeque and the satellite TV were rows of padded benches and some lawn chairs. Behind the deck of this wooden boat sailing in its parking lot sea, between the edge of the asphalt and a swampy-looking inlet, was a huge cream-colored old Daimler Princess, tires rotted off, weeds growing up around the winglike fenders and the wide running boards. Something from another time.

A very black, very skinny man in baggy pants and a moth-eaten wifebeater undershirt was cooking something on the barbeque that was creating enormous amounts of smoke. "Lloyd," said Poitier. "Percy's brother. He owns the motel."

"Where'd he get the car?" asked Hilts.

"The Duke of Windsor," said Poitier. "Creamie-pie leave it here when he left the king's employ. Lloyd been going on about fixing it since 1956. Which is about as much true as Percy been knighted by the Queen. Lloyd's a good man though, General. He won't do you wrong."

"Creamie-pie?" Finn whispered.

"The Duke, I guess," Hilts said and shrugged.

An elderly black woman as skinny and ropy as beef jerky with a face to match came out of one of the motel units wearing bright blue rubber gloves and carrying a red pail with a mop in it. She saw the taxi and waved her free hand. Her smile was more like a grimace of pain.

"Mrs. Amelia Terco herself," Poitier explained. "Mother to Lloyd and to Percy. Does the cleaning for her boys. Looks like her rheumatism's acting up." He laughed. "'Course, it's been acting up since Hemingway came here to bonefish once."

"A little old for that kind of work, isn't she?" Finn asked, startled. The woman was ancient.

"Don't you go telling her that," Poitier said with a laugh. "She bite your head off. Tell you Percy was useless except for lying in Parliament and Lloyd too lazy to clean up after himself, let alone other people." They climbed out of the taxi. Lloyd waved his spatula then went back to staring down into the smoke pouring up from the grill.

"Good mornin', good mornin', how are you this mornin'?" said Poitier to Lloyd Terco, joining him at the barbeque. "Brought you some business."

"Well, that's nice," said Lloyd, squinting through the smoke. "You want some nice grouper, young lady?" he asked, smiling at Finn. The smoke wafted over her. It smelled delicious, and she told him so.

"Get the pretty young thing a plate, Mr. Poitier, and one for her friend as well," instructed the chef in the undershirt. Poitier went to a table laid out in front of the big TV and picked up a couple of paper plates and some plastic cutlery. "He tell you his name was Sidney Poitier?" Lloyd asked.

"He did," Hilts said. "Isn't it?"

"Far as I know," answered Lloyd. "Calling him that since he was six years old, which in his case was a long, long time ago. Just wondered if he brought it up. He usually does. Thinks he gets better tips that way."

Poitier came back with the plates and the utensils.

"Telling lies again, Lloyd Terco?"

"Whenever I can," Lloyd answered. He used the spatula to slide a couple of lightly battered slabs of fish onto the plate. "If I had a deep fryer we'd have some chips or some conch fritters, but I don't so we won't." He pronounced "conch" *konk*. "Sad thing, but I'd burn myself if I had one, so p'raps it's for the best."

Finn sat down on the nearest bench and rested the plate on her knees. She started to cut into fish with the plastic knife and fork.

"Eat it with your fingers, girlie. Mr. Poitier there brought you the knife and fork just to prove we have manners. Won't cook you in a pot or some such."

"No bones in your noses either," said Hilts.

"Those are African niggers, my son. Island niggers got civilized a long time ago," said Poitier blandly. He winked at Finn. She took a bite of the fish and winked back. Poitier liked that. The fish melted in her mouth. She tasted beer and lime. Lloyd handed fish out to everyone and then took some himself. He put his plate down beside one of the lawn chairs, went to the front of the boat and opened up a small fridge under the TV. He uncapped four bottles of Kalik and brought them back to his guests. Finn took a swig. She wasn't much of a beer drinker, but this was like drinking liquid honey.

"Great," she said.

"Funny name," said Hilts, reading the label. He pronounced it *kay-lik*.

Lloyd corrected him. "K'lick," he instructed, just barely separating it into two syllables. "Named after the sound the cowbell in a steel band makes."

Finn took another bite of fish and sipped her beer. A tiny, bright red lizard ran across her foot. She was suddenly a very long way from ten hours in a British Airways 757 eating chicken korma, the pale kid with snot running across his upper lip licking it away every minute or so, staring at her between the seats.

A little bit of a breeze blew up from the inlet. There was a faint smell in the air, an odd mix of rotting vegetation, seaweed, and smoke that should have been a turnoff but was strangely invigorating. Alive in a very simple, basic way. All she wanted to do was take a nap and stop thinking about anything at all, which of course was exactly the reason people came to the Bahamas in the first place. She took another bite of fish. Her plate was empty.

"More," said Lloyd. It wasn't a question. He spatluaed her another few chunks of the battered fish. She ate it and drank more beer. Another lizard ran up the telephone pole. She was in a lizard-infested heaven.

"Gecko," said Lloyd, noticing her glance. "A little tiny alligator without any teeth. *Hemidactylus frenatus*. They eat bugs, keep the rooms spider-free, you know." *Hemidactylus frenatus?* Lloyd had hidden depths, she thought.

Lloyd turned to Hilts. "You want a room, yeah?"

"Yeah."

"Fifty a night if you don't use the AC too much. We watch the games out here if it's good weather. Comes with the room."

"Games?"

"Mostly fights. Tonight it's a couple of middle-weights from Brazil. Eight o'clock. Beer's cheap, popcorn is free." He nodded to Poitier. "Show them a room, Mr. Poitier."

"Sure, General," Poitier said with a nod. He took the overnight bags from them even though they weighed almost nothing and they filed around to the shady side of the big chicken-coop building.

"You're a bellboy too?" Hilts asked.

Poitier shrugged. "He gives me the room on the roof, I bring him customers, take them to the airport or into town. Fair trade." He put down the bags and opened the door with a key that was dangling from the lock with a big number tag on it. Room one. It was in the middle of the row.

"One?"

212

"Eleven. Other number fell off and Lloyd never replaced it."

"There's not eleven rooms in the place."

"Lloyd's got a thing about seven and two so he left them out." He unlocked the door, pushed it open and picked up the bags. They followed him inside. If the outside looked like a Bahamian *Psycho,* the interior of the room fit right in. It had all the ambience of the Bates Motel. Two rust-stained inset laundry sinks for dishes, a gas camping stove for cooking, a pair of lumpy beds, and a sagging ceiling. Bathroom cubicle in the back with a shower stall. The floor was covered with emerald-green Astroturf. "Pretty good for fifty bucks," said Poitier. The old air conditioner in the window was sealed with caulk.

"As long as the roof doesn't fall in," said Hilts.

"Been that way for years, no reason why it should fall down now."

Poitier leaned over the nearest bed and switched on the air conditioner. It wheezed into life and made a noise like a Volkswagen heater in the middle of February.

"Enjoy," said Poitier. He left them alone.

Hilts watched a gecko skitter across the ceiling on gummy little feet that seemed to have suction cups on the toes.

"I like it," said Finn.

"The gecko?"

"The room." She sat down on one of the beds. It sagged even lower. She'd seen worse on archaeological digs with her mother in the Yucatan, but not much worse. "It's homey."

"That's one word for it," Hilts agreed cautiously.

"Hiltons have reservations computers. Data terminals in the rooms. This place doesn't even have telephones. We can't call out. No one can call in. Its cheap and it's safe."

"I guess."

"So how do we find out about the *Acosta Star*?"

"DeVaux's ship?"

"That burned and sank."

"That one." Hilts thought for a moment. "Maybe Lloyd or Sidney know something. They've been around since Creamie-pie, after all."

"I wonder how he got that name," she said and frowned.

"I hate to think," answered Hilts. They went outside and back to the boat. The smoke had cleared. Poitier and Lloyd Terco were sitting down and drinking beer, staring at the old car and the swampy inlet beyond. A few ancient-looking conch boats were staggering out into the open water beyond the inlet, fishermen in shorts and wifebeaters like Lloyd's sitting on the little cabin roofs or crouching by the outboard tillers. Wind blew through the long sawtooth leaves on the palms. You could almost see how it had been before Columbus, a few Carib Indians on the beach, cracking open conchs, stripping out the meat with stone tools, staring out to sea, waiting for genocide to catch them napping.

Hilts and Finn sat down on a bench facing the two men.

Hilts spoke. "Either of you gentlemen know anything about a ship called the *Acosta Star*?"

There was a short silence. The two men exchanged a look and a shrug. It was Lloyd who answered.

"French in the beginning. *Île de France,* I think. Built in 1938 or so. Brand-new and they sunk her in the harbor to keep the Germans from getting her. Dutch after the war. They sold her to the Italians. When me an' Mr. Tibbs here worked on old St. Georges she was called *Bahamian Star* for a few years, flyin' convenience out of Liberia, but then Acosta Lines bought her. Must have been sometime in the late fifties, because they didn't have her long before she burned and went down in Donna."

"Donna?"

"Hurricane. Small and nasty."

"She sank in a hurricane?"

"She caught fire first. Engine room. Got most everyone off and left a skeleton crew to fight the fire. Donna came out of nowhere and she disappeared."

"Where?" Hilts asked.

"If I knew I wouldn't have said disappeared."

"The neighborhood."

Poitier answered. "Some say the Tongue, some say the channel."

"The Tongue?" asked Finn.

"Tongue of the Ocean," explained Lloyd Terco. "Lot of locals just call it Toto. A hole in the water just east of Andros, a hundred miles long and ten thousand feet deep."

"Other people say Donna swept her farther before she sank. Great Bahamas Bank, Old Bahama Channel offshore from Cuba."

"What do you think?" Hilts asked.

"Don't," said Poitier. "Don't bother thinking about something had nothing to do with me so long ago."

"Tuck thinks about it. Talks about it too," offered Lloyd.

"Tuck?"

"Tucker Noe. He'll tell you he saw her go down, right in front of his eyes, off Lobos Cay Light, and that's even farther. Pirates and Cubans and Boomers."

"Boomers?" asked Hilts.

"Nuclear submarines," said Poitier.

"Who's Tucker Noe?" asked Finn.

"Fishing guide. Almost as famous as Bonefish Foley. Between them those two old men bonefished for every president since Lincoln and Ernest Hemingway besides."

"He's still alive?" Hilts asked.

"Hemingway? Naw, he long gone."

Finn smiled as she realized they were ribbing Hilts on purpose and he kept falling for it.

Hilts scowled. "I meant this Tucker Noe."

"Just barely," Lloyd said and laughed.

"Can we talk to him?"

"Sure," said Lloyd. "You can talk but that's not sayin' Tuck goin' to answer."

29

Tucker Noe lived on the south coast of New Providence—the hurricane side, where the winds blew up the channel from the south, or curled in from the open sea to the east. Coral Cay Point stuck out like a bony finger into the pale green sea with mangrove on one side and coral bonefish shallows on the other. The point itself was a neat collection of narrow old docks and walkways that were home to three dozen small fishing boats, a sportfisher or two, and *Spindrift,* once a World War Two minesweeper, then converted into an oceanographic research ship for the University of Florida, and finally turned into a live-aboard salvage and sometime dive boat run by a crew of aging ex-hippies and scuba junkies. Tucker Noe lived in a small shack perched on the end of the *Spindrift* dock beside a pair of old Texaco pumps and directly in front of his own bonefish boat, an unnamed thirty-two-foot cabin flatboat with a roughly made plank cabin sitting on top of the open deck. A worn canvas awning stretched from the cabin to the transom. The transom itself was fitted with two old-fashioned Evinrude outboards, both with their covers off and the guts of the engines exposed. A very old man was sitting on a plastic-webbed lawn chair under the awning with a homemade plywood table in front of him. The table was painted with checkerboard squares of red and black. A set of homemade chess pieces roughly carved from dark and pale coral were set out on the board. There were only a few pieces in each color left in play. A letter on blue airmail paper lay to one side.

"Idiot," muttered the old man, a gnarled finger pushing his king forward. "He takes me for a fool?" He glanced at the letter and shook his head in disgust.

"I'll be damned," whispered Hilts, staring down at the board as they stepped aboard the old boat. "That's the Opera House Massacre, or close to it."

Sidney Poitier made the introductions, then eased his backside down on the boat's wide gunwale with a sigh.

"You know something about chess, sir?" asked Tucker Noe.

"Some," Hilts said.

"What's the Opera House Massacre?" Finn asked.

"A famous game in Paris, at the Opera House there," explained the photographer. "An American chess player named Paul Morphy was challenged to a game by the Duke of Brunswick and a count something or other."

"Isouard was his name," the old man supplied. His voice carried an educated English accent touched by the faint lilt of the islands. His skin was black and very wrinkled, even the smooth skin of his palms set out with a web of tiny creases. He looked as though he'd been out in the sun for a century, which was probably fairly close to being accurate.

"That's right. Anyway it was 1858. They were watching the *Barber of Seville*. Morphy was in a hurry to see the rest of the opera so he beat the two men playing against him together during the intermission. Morphy was the first international grandmaster from America. They didn't have a chance." Hilts pointed to the roughly made chessboard. "That's how the game turned out."

"You have an excellent eye," said the old man.

"It's a famous game."

"If you know about famous chess games. It's not like playing Grand Theft Auto Four on a PlayStation," said Tucker Noe.

"I gave up after version number two," Hilts said with a smile.

"I have many grandchildren and great-grandchildren. Even a few great-great-grandchildren." The old man laughed. "I'm an expert at stealing cars and assassinating prostitutes on the streets of Liberty City, or wherever it is on the latest version. It seems to be a necessary talent these days, even here in our island paradise."

"They're lookin' for the *Acosta Star*," said Sidney Poitier. There was a long silence.

"You're divers," Tucker Noe said with a sigh.

"Not really," said Finn. "We're interested in a passenger who might have been aboard on her last voyage."

"Family?"

"No."

"The *Acosta Star* was no treasure galleon," Tucker Noe cautioned. "She was an early cruise ship."

"We're aware of that," answered Hilts. "The ship is part of a puzzle we're trying to figure out. It's a bit of a life-and-death thing," he added, frowning.

"I'm becoming curious." The old man smiled. "Not something that happens often to men of advanced years like me or Mr. Poitier here."

"Speak for yourself, old man," the taxi driver snorted.

"I generally do," answered Tucker Noe. "When I'm forced to by the stupidity of others." He arched an eyebrow at his friend, who arched an eyebrow back. Finn was beginning to wonder if there was anyone under eighty living on the whole island. She glanced toward the other side of the dock and saw a muscular, blond-haired man in a T-shirt clambering up the gangway on the side of the *Spindrift*, Tucker Noe's neighbor. Definitely in the under-thirty class. She smiled at her little private thought.

"His name is probably Tab," said Hilts, who'd spotted the man as well. Not such a private thought after all.

"Actually his name is Dolf van Delden. His late father was the *Spindrift*'s owner," said Tucker Noe. "Dutch, from Amsterdam. I don't ask beyond that."

"Interesting people you have here."

"Places like New Providence have always attracted interesting people. How many countries have a motto like 'Pirates Expelled, Commerce Restored'?"

"You make it sound like there's some question of that."

"Jury's still out on the pirate issue. Time was they had names like Morgan and Teach. Now it's Escobar and Rodriguez."

"We were talking about the *Acosta Star*," interrupted Finn.

"That's so." The old man nodded.

"Sidney here said you saw her go down," said Finn. "In a hurricane."

"Donna," Tucker Noe said, nodding. "She was in the eye, burning like a candle. I was making for Guinchos Cay or Cay Lobos before I sank myself."

"You were out in a hurricane in this?" said Hilts.

"She was the *Malahat*. Old Chris-Craft fish boat I used to take charters out on."

"A fishing charter in a hurricane?"

"Other business. And you've clearly never been in a hurricane. They have a tendency to come out of nowhere, just like Donna."

"What other business?" Finn asked.

"None of yours," answered Tucker Noe with a crisp edge to his voice.

"Oh," said Finn, suddenly understanding what the other business was.

"You just leave it at that." He glanced at Poitier. "I have changed my ways since then," he added stiffly.

"Bull crap." The taxi driver laughed. "You just changed your methods, old man."

"Nevertheless," said Tucker Noe, turning back to Hilts.

The photographer waved dismissively. "No problem. This was at night?"

"That's right."

Simpson had said eleven at night, Finn remembered. It seemed as though his information was on the mark.

"How did you know it was the *Acosta Star*?" asked Finn.

"I didn't, not right then," answered Tucker Noe. "Though I had my suspicions."

"No radio?" asked Hilts.

"I had one, but no one was calling on it," said the old man.

"And presumably you were ducking under the radar," said Hilts.

"This was 1960, young man. There wasn't much in the way of radar at all back then. The Bay of Pigs was still almost a year away. I doubt if Señor Castro had a gallon of gasoline to spare for patrol boats. The *Acosta Star* was a torch, not a spy ship or any kind of threat."

"Did you try to help?"

"No, I stayed clear. There was no sign of life, you could see that the davits were all swung out, lines in the water, lifeboats gone. A ghost ship."

"Was she under power?" Hilts asked.

"Hard to say. Maybe. The swells were very bad. She might have stayed afloat for a long time if it hadn't been for the hurricane. I reached Cay Lobos just before midnight. There's an old lighthouse there. I beached *Malahat* on the lee shore and went up the tower just before the weather broke again."

"What happened?"

"The hull had obviously been weakened. She broached and broke in half toward the stern. She was gone in less than a minute."

"No survivors?"

"As I said, she was a hulk. Everyone capable of getting off was obviously gone. There was no one left on board to survive."

"*Acosta Star* was a big ship. How come no one ever found her?"

"She was a big ship but it's a bigger ocean. I was the only one to see her go. Most wouldn't have put her that far south or west. By rights she should have gone down in the Tongue, which is where most people think she is. Down in the deep." He paused. "But she's not." The old man plucked the dark, carved coral king off the chessboard and twirled it between a gnarled old thumb and forefinger. "She's in a little more than fifteen fathoms—her keel at a hundred feet maybe—lying on a sandy bottom in the shadow of a place called No-Name Reef. You could fly over her at wave height and never see her unless it was just the right time of day. Not that it matters any now."

"Why's that?" Hilts asked.

"'Cause no one ever goes to No-Name Reef no more," Poitier answered.

"Why's that?" said Finn.

"Because No-Name Reef is in disputed Cuban territorial waters," responded Tucker Noe. "It's not 1960 any longer. There's lots of patrol boats and lots of radar these days. The only other people traveling in those waters are coke runners in 'go-fast' boats outward bound from Barranquilla or Santa Marta on the Colombian coast, and they're usually better armed than the Cubans or the DEA. The *Acosta Star* is in a war zone."

"Maybe your friend could help," suggested Poitier. "The writer fellow. As I understand, he knows that old ship inside and out."

Tucker Noe threw his friend a warning glance but the taxi driver ignored him. "Lives out there all alone on Hollaback Cay, must be bored out of his skull. You and that Mills character went out to the wreck a few times, didn't you, old man?"

"Lyman Mills? That writer?" asked Finn. "The one they used to call the poor man's James Michener?" Lyman Aloysius Mills had virtually invented the idea of the beach bestseller. As a teenager Finn had read her mother's creased and spine-cracked hand-me-down copies, inhaling them like hot buttered popcorn.

"Man owns a private island in the Bahamas don't qualify as a poor man's anything in my book," said Sidney Poitier with a laugh.

"That Mills?" Hilts repeated.

"That's the one," said Tucker Noe with a nod.

30

Lyman Mills would have been a perfect example of the glamorous American success story except for the fact that he wasn't really American; he only seemed that way. The son of a British soldier who had been cashiered for refusing to fight with the North Russian Expeditionary Force after spending three years in the trenches of France and Belgium, Mills immigrated to Canada as a child, spending much of his childhood in Halifax and then Toronto, where his father worked as a waiter and his mother ran a boardinghouse.

In a number of interviews given over the years, Mills said he could never remember a time when he hadn't wanted to be a writer. He dropped out of school early, spent his early years as a copy boy at the *Toronto Star* hearing stories about Hemingway and Callahan from the previous war, and finally quit the paper to join the Royal Air Force Coastal Command, where he flew, and fell in love with, the Grumman Widgeon, a four-seater patrol flying boat that was a miniature version of the huge Pan Am Clippers that spanned the globe.

After the war, married and with a child on the way, Mills went to work for an advertising company and specialized in writing copy for liquor ads. This led to his first novel, originally entitled *Aged in Oak,* but eventually called *The Label,* an insider's look at the workings of a huge distillery, following its fortunes over several generations, including through Prohibition. Seven hundred and eighty-eight single-spaced pages' worth.

When half a dozen Canadian publishers turned it down as being too "racy" and "crude," with little or no "socially redeeming content," Mills climbed on board the overnight train to New York with the four-and-a-half-pound manuscript under his arm and sold it to the first publisher he saw on Fifth Avenue. The only suggestion his editor had was that he type double-spaced in the future for the sake of everyone's eyesight.

Thus began Lyman Mills's skyrocketing career as an extoller of everyday things and people, from the post office *(The Letter),* to automobiles *(The Car),* to buildings *(The Tower)* and the weapons industry *(The Gun).* One book a year, year in and year out, for three decades, stories filled with a simple formula of sex, adventure, action, and lots of interesting facts all tied together with page-turning plots. As one critic put it, "Lyman Mills may not stand the literary tests of time but he sure gets you through those hot summer days at the beach." Reviewers scoffed and no one admitted to buying him in paperback, let alone hardcover, but somehow he wound up selling millions of copies, hard and soft, in seventy-five countries and thirty-eight languages. He wrote more than thirty instant bestsellers, all of which were made into movies or TV miniseries and in one case both. Along the way he indulged his old love and found his mistress, JS996, which he renamed *Daffy* after the Walter Lantz cartoon duck, a World War Two Widgeon based in Nassau during the war, and found in a Miami junkyard. Restoring the old seaplane to pristine shape became the passion of his later years, and he and his long-suffering wife, Terry, used *Daffy* to fly all over the Caribbean.

Then, after the death of Terry, a day before the horrible events of 9/11, Lyman Mills just quit. Physically in perfect health even into his eighties, the writer told an interviewer that the loss of his wife had broken his heart and he'd simply had enough of everything, writing included. He retired permanently to his estate on Hollaback Cay and was never seen in public again.

Hollaback Cay was a seventy-eight-acre island twenty miles south of New Providence with a main beach, its own reef, two rainwater cisterns, a 220-volt solar power generator, and a hurricane-proof harbor for sheltering large boats and *Daffy* the seaplane.

The house stood on a dramatic limestone outcropping on a low hill above the little harbor, facing out to sea. It was modest for a man of Mills's means, a simple U-shaped bungalow with a narrow swimming pool in the sheltered courtyard and large open arches that brought the outside in. The walls were all in light shades, the floor cool, natural stone, and the furniture modern. There was art everywhere, Picasso, Léger, Dubuffet, Georgia O'Keeffe, and others, all real and most of them priceless. Where there wasn't art there were bookcases crammed with titles ranging from Simon Schama's magnificent art-history biography *Rembrandt's Eyes* to the latest John Grisham. One whole wall of the spacious living room was filled with nothing but various foreign editions of Mills's own work, hundreds of them.

The author sat on a long canvas-colored couch and sipped a glass of iced tea brought to him by Arthur, his very British and unexpectedly Caucasian servant. Mills looked like a very well-tanned and slightly less muscular version of Sean Connery, right down to the thinning, snow-white hair, the gray beard, and the trademark jet-black eyebrows. Unlike Connery's deep brown bedroom eyes, however, Lyman Mills's were as blue as the seascape in front of him. His accent was different too, not British plums, Canadian twang, or American drawl, but a flat, uninflected mid-Atlantic mixture of all three. Like his writing, the voice was approachable, nonthreatening, and intelligent, a gentle baritone. He would have made a perfect announcer on National Public Radio. He wore khakis, an open-collared white cotton shirt and blue deck shoes without socks. Nothing he wore had a monogram on it and everything could have come off the rack at JC Penney.

"It's an interesting story," he said, putting his tea down on the big glass-and-bamboo coffee table in front of him. There was a litter of up-to-date magazines and the Book Review section from the previous week's Sunday *New York Times* on the coffee table as well; Mills might be a recluse, but he was still in touch with the world. "Mind you," he continued, "I don't think I believed a word of it until you mentioned the name Devereaux in connection with the *Acosta Star*."

"I'm not sure I understand," said Finn.

"Just a moment." Mills got up and left the room. He returned a few moments later carrying several thick file folders. He sat down and dumped the folders on the coffee table.

"I've had a lot of people try to con me over the years— I've been researching a book and had people outright lie

228

to me—but one thing they always had in common was an inability to get the details right." He smiled at them across the table. "Someone once asked Stephen King how he wrote a book and he answered 'one word at a time.' Never a truer word was said. It's all in the words, the details—not so much the facts—the details. I spent the better part of ten years off and on researching the *Acosta Star*. It was the story I was working on when I quit. Going to call it *The Ship*... what else?" He smiled again. He flipped open one of the file folders, but it was obvious he knew the material by heart.

"There were three hundred and twenty passengers and a hundred and ninety-four crew members aboard the *Star* when she left Nassau on the sixth of September. She was supposed to sail down to San Juan, then Santo Domingo, and finally Kingston, Jamaica, before heading back to Miami. It was a standard cruise, she'd made the trip plenty of times. The fire broke out after a boiler explosion. Eight crew members were killed outright, three more in the fire. Fourteen passengers were killed and accounted for. Six just never turned up. One of them was Peter Devereaux. Nobody trying to lie to me, or just trying to pull the wool over my eyes, would have known that name or his background. Particularly since Devereaux was always one of my favorites."

"Favorites?" Finn asked.

"A novelist who writes about historical events, even when they're fictionalized, is always looking for holes to fill, missing pieces," explained Mills. "That was Devereaux. He came aboard in Nassau. That was strange enough—most people boarded in Miami, there was no real airport then—but when I started delving into his history I found out he didn't have one; everything dead-ended when I tried to find out about him pre-University of Kansas. The only real connection I could find was to Switzerland, and maybe Italy before that. I also found out from a few survivors who'd met him on board that he spoke Italian like a native. There was another missing person on the ship who turned out to be a 'hole' as well, a man named Marty Kerzner traveling on a Canadian passport. Except the passport was a phony. Given the way Israeli Intelligence likes to use Canadian passports for her agents, I put two and two together and came up with five: for the purposes of the book I made Devereaux an Italian war criminal who was personally responsible for the deaths of several hundred Beta Israel Ethiopian Jewish orphans in Addis Ababa—a story that still needs to be told, I might add; not much written on the subject of Italian war criminals—and made Marty Kerzner into Martin Coyne, who is actually based on a real Mossad assassin named Moses 'Boogie' Yaalon." He beamed another one of his pleasant, slightly melancholy smiles in their direction.

"Complicated," murmured Hilts.

"Ever talk to the legal department of a publishing company? Or someone from the staff of Oprah? You've got to cover your ass, sir, believe me." He laughed, but the humor had a bitter tinge to it. "I haven't written a new book in years, but I still have to talk to my agent at least twice a week and my lawyer almost as often. Somebody's always trying to sue me. The last time it was an illiterate lunatic from the Fulton Fish Market who thought that I'd based one of my unsavory characters on his life story."

"How did that turn out for you?"

"My lawyer suggested to his lawyer that if his client would be willing to admit in public to doing some of the unsavory things my character had done, then he might have a case, and maybe twenty to life in Ossining as well."

"So what do you think really happened to Peter Devereaux?" Finn asked, reining in the writer's slightly meandering story. "Do you think there was any real connection between him and this Kerzner fellow?"

Mills took another sip of iced tea and leaned back against the pale couch cushions. "All I know for sure is that they both have suspicious backgrounds and that neither one of them was rescued before the hurricane and brought to the naval station in Key West." He gestured toward the files on the coffee table. "I've got the list right there."

"What about this Bishop Principe, is he on the list?"

"Yes. He was one of the ones who died during the fire."

"What do you think happened to them?" Finn asked.

The old writer scratched delicately at his scalp, as though he was afraid of dislodging the last few wisps of hair floating almost invisibly across it. "Well, dear, before you and your pilot friend came along and screwed up my plot with your tall tale, I'd have said that they simply died in the explosion or the subsequent fire and were overlooked, but now I'm not so sure."

"Somebody must have done a head count," said Hilts. "You'd think it would have been a standard safety procedure."

"It was," replied Mills. "I had a lengthy telephone conversation with Capitan Francisco Crevicas, the master of the *Acosta Star*. He ran the check himself. A party of crew members checked every stateroom, every deck.

Everyone was accounted for. He said that after everyone was off they stayed with the ship for more than an hour. He said by then some of the deck plates were glowing cherry red from the flames and paint was peeling off the hull in huge chunks. According to him no one could have survived."

"Where was this?"

"Twenty miles south and slightly east of Curley Cut Cays. That's the tip of Andros Island. According to the captain the fire broke out just as they were coming off the Tongue of the Ocean."

"What did I tell you?" said Tucker Noe, speaking for the first time since they'd arrived.

"If you learn nothing else from your experience here," said Mills, "learn that Bonefish Tucker Noe is always correct, right, Mr. Noe?"

"Always key-wreck, that's key-wreck, Mistah Mills," the old man answered with a smile and an outrageously put-on Bahamian accent.

Mills swooshed the ice cubes around in his empty glass. "You've asked me a lot of questions," he said, looking at Finn. "Now I'd like to ask a few of my own."

"Shoot," said Finn. She glanced at Hilts, sitting beside her across from the white-haired writer. "We've got nothing to hide."

"As the unfortunate Mr. Lennon once said, everyone's got something to hide," responded Mills. "But that aside, can you tell me why you think your Mr. Adamson would be pursuing you so energetically. I met the man once or twice at cocktail parties and charity functions. He never struck me as being a homicidal maniac. You seem to be saying that the man is involved in some long-running criminal conspiracy involving stolen religious artifacts. It's a little far-fetched, you'll have to admit."

Hilts answered. "Rolf Adamson comes from a long line of hyper-Christians. In his book, if it's done in the name of Christ, it's automatically 'right.'"

Mills smiled. "Hyper-Christian. Interesting term. You think he's on some sort of crusade?"

"It worked for Richard the Lionheart. In his mind some kind of groundswell response to terrorism is just what the doctor ordered."

"Fire with fire, that sort of thing?"

"And an eye for an eye."

"Imperialism disguised as self-defense?"

"Something like that. We can invade everyone from Grenada to Afghanistan, but if anyone spills a drop of our blood, it's terrorism."

"Now we're talking politics," Mills said and smiled.

"I wouldn't be surprised if politics wasn't what it's all about," said Hilts. "Big power, big money, big politics."

"Adamson?"

"Why not?" Hilts shrugged. "He uses this so-called Lucifer Gospel as a political device to rally around. The whole theory he's putting out is that Christ spent his last days in the real promised land, America, which by definition makes Americans the real Chosen People."

"Given the time frame it would probably make the chosen people members of the Algonquian tribe, if my knowledge of Native people is reliable."

"The people from the Bible Belt could overlook that," said Hilts. "Christ was an American; quite a platform for a fundamentalist political party. According to Adamson, the Lucifer Gospel is the one thing the Bible is missing: the teachings of Christ in his own words."

"You truly think that's what this is about?"

"Adamson's got the background for it, and the ambition. He also has the money to make it happen. We've been heading in this direction since Reagan. Getting the United States back to its Puritan, witch-burning roots."

"It's still very hard to believe. According to you this man Hisnawi is involved. A Libyan, a Muslim. How do you explain that?"

"The same way you explain Iran, Iraq, even Venezuela and Cuba. Oil. Money. A deal. Who knows? Adamson's got a lot of money and he's been spreading it around. He got the license to launch a new dig in the desert for a reason, and it wasn't to locate the remains of a Coptic monastery. Maybe Hisnawi wants to be the next dictator of Libya after he takes out Qaddafi, who's getting pretty long in the tooth these days, I might add."

"You've got it all figured out, don't you?" said Mills.

Hilts nodded. "I've given it a lot of thought."

"And you, Miss Ryan, where do you fit into all of this?"

"I'm not sure. At first I thought it might just have been a matter of being in the wrong place at the wrong time. Now I'm not so sure."

"You believe Mr. Hilts's story?"

"I'm still with him, aren't I? And Simpson's involvement seems to be through me, or my father. I don't have all the answers yet."

"And you think those answers might be on the *Acosta Star*?"

"Some of them. One thing I do know is that we're in a hurry. The passports we're using aren't going to last forever. We need proof to take to the authorities. At least something to show that we didn't have anything to do with Vergadora's murder. The ship is the next step, that much is clear."

"I don't think your Martin Kerzner with the Canadian passport and Peter Devereaux not turning up as a survivor is a coincidence any more than you do, Mr. Mills." Hilts offered his own smile. "And I think you're curious as hell to find out."

The writer lifted his glass, took one of the ice cubes and cracked it between a set of remarkably strong teeth for a man of his years. He chewed on the broken chips for a moment, then swallowed. He put the glass down on the table again with a hard clunk.

"We'll need something stronger than iced tea and lemon." He grinned, then turned and looked back over his shoulder. Almost by magic Arthur the servant immediately appeared.

"Yes, sir?" the man said, shimmering into the room.

"Do we have any Kaliks in the refrigerator, Arthur?"

"I'm sure we do, sir."

"Then why don't you fetch us some," said Mills. "Then my new friends and I can get down to work."

31

The seaplane flew low over the dark, rich blue of the Caribbean at just over a hundred knots, the sculpted boat hull of the fuselage less than five hundred feet above the calm rolling sea. The sky above the high-set wings was almost perfectly clear, and the horizon ahead was a sharp, steady line except for a speeding dark island of squall far to the west.

Daffy's two big Lycoming engines filled the cockpit with a steady, powerful roar, and the plane seemed to fly by itself. Hilts's fingers on the old-fashioned throw-over yoke barely exerted any pressure, his free hand only rarely reaching up to the overhead knobs and throttles to make an occasional adjustment. They were an hour and a half out of Hollaback Cay, heading south above the Tongue of the Ocean.

They'd spent the better part of a week preparing for their dive on the *Acosta Star,* shuttling back and forth between Hollaback Cay and Nassau gathering equipment, including the bright yellow Inspiration Closed Circuit Rebreathers packed into the cargo area behind them. They'd gone to the library and museum on Shirley Street and studied the archives files of the *Nassau Guardian,* researching the *Acosta Star* and the details of her sinking almost fifty years before. They also spent a great deal of

time with Tucker Noe, taking notes about the area immediately surrounding the dive site and consulting Lyman
Mills's personal chart library. According to the old bonefish guide the ship wouldn't be hard to find if they knew
what to look for; he'd taken accurate bearings from the
old lighthouse, and while the sunken hull was hidden in
the lee of the reef for twenty-three hours a day, there were
several identifying markers on the reef itself that, seen from
the air, would enable them to pinpoint the location to
within a few hundred yards. It was Noe's estimation that a
dive of only forty feet or so would put them on the main
deck of the ship.

Over the years Lyman Mills had collected an impressive collection of *Acosta Star* memorabilia, including old
cruise brochures, schedules, and passenger lists, engi-
neering drawings of the ship's construction, and half a
dozen photo albums from passengers who'd cruised on the
ship at various times during her career. One of the most
useful of these had been a detailed set of scrapbooks that
once belonged to Paulus Boegarts, or Paul Bogart, as he
liked to be called, a half Dutch, half American who'd been
professionally associated with the ship through almost all
of her incarnations. Using all of this information Finn,
Hilts, Lyman Mills, and Tucker Noe spent several days
and nights developing a strategy for the underwater pene-
tration of the vessel.

The M.V. *Acosta Star* was by far the largest vessel ever to
have sunk in the Caribbean. At 758 feet overall and 37,000
gross tons, she was 150 feet longer and 1,800 tons heavier
than her nearest rival, the *Bianca C.,* which had gone
down just off the coast of Grenada. By wreck diving stan-
dards the *Acosta Star* was a monster, and like any monster

it would have to be treated with caution, care, and a great deal of respect. A ship a hundred feet wide and the length of two and a half football fields would have been confusing in broad daylight with a deck plan; after fifty years and a hundred feet down in the deep-seas gloom, the interior of the vessel was going to be a very dark, dangerous, sharp-edged and coral-encrusted labyrinth.

In theory the dive didn't pose any insoluble problems. The bottom depth was a hundred feet in clear water, an easy depth even for simple scuba. With rebreathers they would have almost triple the time they'd have with ordinary tanks—better than three hours—and with their constant mix of oxygen and nitrogen, the rebreathers gave them even more time by removing the need to decompress on the way up. They'd be wearing full face masks with Ocean Technology Buddy Phones to let them communicate underwater and have the best tank-mounted and handheld lighting units available. They even had a GEM systems portable magnetometer that would ping for the wreck, find it, and instantly provide its exact location via the Global Positioning System.

According to the passenger lists, Bishop Principe had taken the Gelderland Deluxe Suite on the Upper Promenade Deck. Pierre DeVaux, alias Peter Devereaux, had occupied cabin A-305, one level below the Main Deck on the port, or left, side of the ship, about one hundred and fifty feet from the bow of the ship and two decks below Bishop Principe. Given the way the ship had reportedly gone down, this would put Devereaux's cabin on the "outer," ocean side of the reef. Martin Kerzner, the supposed Israeli Intelligence agent traveling on the false Canadian passport, had been on the deck below

Devereaux in cabin B-616 on the inner, or reef side of the ship. To go from one cabin to the other would involve entering the ship through one of the main hull hatches leading into the *Acosta Star*'s central lobby, located on either side of the ship. From there they would follow the wide lobby stairs up to Bishop Principe's suite on the Upper Promenade Deck, then down to Devereaux's cabin on A Deck. If necessary they could then use the lobby stairs again to descend to B Deck.

If the stairs were blocked by debris, they had two alternate routes: one down the purser's companionway, the other using one of the two elevator shafts on the port and starboard sides of the lobby. Theoretically it was a walk in the park.

"You realize that realistically this whole thing is insane, don't you?" Hilts said. "You've never done any wreck diving at all."

"I used to free dive into cenotes in the jungles of Quintana Roo. Two hundred feet," Finn countered. "How long can you hold your breath, Hilts?"

"That's not the point," the pilot answered.

"That's exactly the point. I've used scuba and rebreathers, my dive limit is around two hundred and fifty feet, and on top of that I've done cave diving, which is at least as complicated as wreck diving, and you know it."

"It's too dangerous."

"For a woman? Is that what you're saying?" Finn queried hotly.

"No, of course not, but…"

"No buts."

"I'll need someone on the surface."

"You'll need someone below. It's the prime directive, you know that too: never dive alone."

"This isn't some safety-groomed resort wreck, Finn. It's not going to have all the dangerous spots neatly defanged. Remember, Tucker said there were sharks as well. Tigers. Bulls, mean ones."

"Which is why we brought along shark repellent and a pair of Mares air guns. Relax, Hilts. I can handle myself. In the Roo I had to deal with snakes as thick as your arm and spiders the size of dinner plates. That doesn't include the fire ants and the really gross scorpions. Relax, you'll live longer," she repeated.

"All right," he muttered, but he didn't seem to relax at all. Finn stared out through the side window of the airplane. More than once she'd found herself wondering why they were making the dive at all; the chance that they'd find anything on board after almost fifty years was minimal. When you got right down to it, what could you find? DeVaux, or Devereaux, had apparently discovered something that he thought was evidence that Luciferus Africanus had somehow traveled from the deserts of Libya to the central United States, perhaps bringing the Lucifer Gospel with him on his journey.

Unless the mysterious monk had brought a physical artifact to prove his claim, or explicit directions to where such artifacts could be found, they would be no further ahead. Rolf Adamson and his people had set them up for the violent killing of Vergadora, both to hide the knowledge of Pedrazzi's murder in the desert and to compromise anything they might discover about Devereaux's find. Without the Gospel, or at the very least a clue to its whereabouts, they would have no evidence of Adamson's motive for killing Vergadora and attacking them.

The only other option left to them if the dive came up empty would be to go to Lawrence, Kansas, and see if there was any trace of Devereaux's discovery there. It was possible that he'd left some kind of clue at the Wilcox Classical Museum at the university, but once again, a lot of time had passed. The chances were very slim.

"Check the GPS," said Hilts, peering out through the windscreen. "We should almost be there."

Finn checked the readout on the little box mounted on her side of the cockpit: 22°25'N, 77°40'W." She relayed the numbers to Hilts.

"Then we are there," Hilts said. "Look for the lighthouse."

And suddenly it was there, less than a mile away, a solid white line against the sky poking up from the rough scrub of a coral cay no more than a hundred yards long, the lee end trailing off into a line of breakers and foam that marked the low breaking edge of a reef. The reef itself stretched away, slightly curving, the breakers marking its course for three-quarters of a mile, pointing almost due west toward the coast of Cuba. Hilts knew that with another five hundred feet of altitude he would be able to see the coast no more than ten or twelve miles away. It wasn't a particularly comforting thought, even with the Bahamian markings and the idiotic cartoon duck painted in full color on the nose. *Daffy* wasn't going to impress a Cuban Flogger-B MiG armed with Kedge-class laser-guided air-to-surface missiles. He had a vague memory of the payload. About seven hundred pounds of high explosive. Each.

"I'm putting her down," he said nervously.

Finn kept her eyes on the glittering, sun-splashed surface of the shimmering ocean in front of them. Maintaining a steady eighty miles per hour, Hilts dropped the nose evenly and took them down to zero feet. Still keeping up the speed, he touched her down, the keel of the boat hull biting into the highest wavelet of the negligible chop.

The initial stutter and shakes turned into rattling machine guns and then pounding fists and hammers as the hull skipped over the surface before surrendering the lift of the wings to the buoyant hull. As Hilts throttled back the Lycomings on the wings above them, *Daffy* settled into the water, an ugly duckling once again after his brief flight as a swan. Pushing the rudder and easing the yoke to the left, Hilts turned the aircraft and headed them closer to the tiny island.

"Keep an eye out for any broken water or signs of a reef," the pilot warned. They pulled around until the lighthouse was dead ahead, a tall white pillar burning in the sun, topped by a slightly smaller bright red turret marking the light itself. Twenty yards to the right of the slightly flared base of the structure was a small windowless hut. The walls of the little building were whitewash bright, the roof terra-cotta red. Twenty yards farther still and they could see the gray-brown bulk of a rough concrete jetty. There was a clear line visible between the deep ocean and the lighter blue green that marked the shallow water of the reef. If the *Acosta Star* was almost flush against the coral wall, the way Tucker Noe said, it would be almost invisible unless they were right on top of it.

"How close are we going to get?" asked Finn.

"Just on to the shallows, give something for the anchor to bite into. The Widgeon's got a real shallow draft, but I don't want to take any chances. We can take the inflatable in to shore." Packed into a suitcase-sized carrier was a ten-foot Aquastar dive dinghy with a separate, battery-powered ten-horsepower short-shaft outboard.

He finally switched off *Daffy*'s engines and they slid easily toward the shore, barely buffeted by the light breezes. Finn slipped back into the rear compartment, popped the hatch, and grabbed the anchor. At Hilts's signal she dropped the twin shovel device and paid out the line. The anchor bit cleanly at fifteen feet and Finn cleated down the line. *Daffy* turned into the wind, riding easily on the calm water. Twenty minutes after that, the dinghy inflated with its electric pump, and with the little battery-powered outboard clamped to the rubber boat's plastic transom, they scooted in to shore.

"Washed up on a desert island," said Hilts as they reached the coral shingle and hopped out onto the narrow, quartz sand beach.

"Hardly that," Finn said and laughed. The sand was almost uncomfortably hot under her feet, and even with her sunglasses on she had to squint. "According to the charts we're fifteen miles east of Cuba and right on the edge of one of the main shipping channels from South America."

"You're spoiling the fantasy," moaned Hilts melodramatically. "Sun-baked island, beautiful woman... what more could a guy want?"

"In the first place, get a life, and then get the water, the rest of the diving gear, and the magnetometer array, which is back in the airplane. You're going to have to make another trip," she said with a grin.

"What about you?"

"I'm the beautiful woman, remember? I think I'll go exploring and then wait for the big he-man to catch us lunch."

They spent the next hour settling in. The hut was a miniature slum, filled with junk from passers-by, including Cuban boat people who'd scrawled their own version of *Viva Fidel* on the inner walls. A shipwrecked crew of Haitian refugees had left behind chalked messages in French and the dried-out remains of a dead cat. The floor was littered with everything from the ashes of a long-dead fire to an ancient copy of *Fortune* magazine with a feature story extolling the management style of pre-scandal Enron. Finn found a jumbo-size empty box of Nigerian Fele-Fele condoms and a four-color pamphlet from the Buff Divers nude scuba diving association head office in Katy, Texas.

"I guess we weren't the first," said Finn, flipping through the brochure.

"Crossroads of the world," said Hilts, lugging their dive gear under cover and wrinkling his nose at the faint, musky odor given off by the dead tabby in the corner. "If we had time I'd clean the place out." In her exploration Finn had discovered that the lighthouse itself was locked up tight; their was no light keeper, so the light was either automatic or out of service. The padlock on the door looked reasonably new and the woodwork seemed well maintained, so she was betting on automatic.

"It might get a little cool at night," Hilts commented. "Maybe we should sleep on the plane."

"I'd rather camp on the beach," said Hilts. "We've got sleeping bags."

"Whatever." The pilot shrugged. It was obvious he didn't like the idea.

"What's the matter, afraid of wild boars or something?" Finn asked.

"*Daffy*'s our only way off this chunk of coral; I'd like to stay close, that's all."

"We're a long way from Libya," said Finn.

"You think Adamson's forgotten all about us?" Hilts responded. "They slaughtered Vergadora in his villa and they tried to kill us in Paris. These people are serious."

"What are they after? It's not like we found some kind of buried treasure."

"If I was going to put money on it I'd say that thing you have around your neck," answered Hilts, pointing to the Lucifer medallion. She'd bought a chain for it at a jewelry shop in Nassau.

"Kill for this?" she scoffed, fingering the silver-dollar-sized medallion.

"Kill for what it means. You heard that old rabbi in Italy. There's been lots of speculation about Luciferus Africanus and his legion over the years, but that's the first hard evidence. It's proof of his theory, or Adamson thinks so. At the very least it's the kind of thing that could get some interest going, maybe some scholarly competition, and I think he'd be willing to kill if he could stop that."

"You think he's that crazy?"

"It seems to run in his family. Schuyler Grand insisted that Franklin Delano Roosevelt was a Jew, a communist, and the Antichrist all wrapped up in one. Great place to start a political dynasty."

"I'm hungry. What did you catch us for lunch, O great hunter?"

"Here," he answered. He reached into a cooler at his feet and threw Finn a foil-wrapped bundle. She snatched it out of the air, found a place at the edge of the beach to sit down, and unwrapped the package.

"Peanut butter?"

Hilts sat down beside her and handed her a dewy can of Kalik. She popped the top and took a sip of the ice-cold, honey-flavored beer.

"Arthur wanted to make us something exotic with cilantro and kiwi fruit in it. Peanut butter sounded more efficient."

"The Wonder Bread's a nice touch. I'm surprised he had it."

"So was I. Arthur refers to it as one of his master's 'aberrations.' Apparently Mills insists on egg-salad sandwiches made with Miracle Whip on Wonder Bread. Drives Arthur nuts."

"I'd say so," said Finn, and took another sip of the Kalik.

"He's eighty-six or something. Doesn't seem to have hurt."

"Good genes."

"I've got a theory," said Hilts, tearing off a chunk of his own sandwich and chewing thoughtfully as he stared out toward the reef. "Health food is like chiropractors. Once you start on either you get addicted, you wind up in some kind of weird symbiosis with them. People who believe in magnets and crystals and high colonics and feng shui too. Best to stay away from them in the first place before you catch them like some kind of disease."

"And you think Rolf Adamson is crazy," she said and laughed.

"What I really think is that single-minded obsessive and very rich people can be dangerous. They start to believe that just because they think something is right and true makes it so. What Senator William Fulbright once referred to as the arrogance of power."

"So how are we supposed to fight against that?" Finn responded wearily. "He's got everything and we've got nothing."

"In the same speech Fulbright quoted an old Chinese proverb: 'In shallow waters dragons become the prey of shrimp.'" He shrugged. "He was talking about Vietnam and American vulnerability in a war we didn't know how to fight, but maybe the same thing applies here; we can do things Adamson can't. We can fly under the radar while he's always in the spotlight."

"You're just trying to make me feel better and change the subject at the same time."

"I'm not sure I even know what the subject was."

"Your approval of Wonder Bread. Which is disgusting, by the way."

"We couldn't all be brought up in whole-grain heaven in... where was it, Columbus?"

"That's right," she answered. She looked out over the sea, then turned to Hilts, a serious expression on her face. "Are we kidding ourselves about this? A ship that's been missing for half a century, evidence of something that's just a myth to the rest of the world? Why us when no one else has managed to find it over the last two thousand years?"

"I used to know a guy who bought lottery tickets all the time. I told him he was crazy, the odds were stacked against him, he didn't stand a hope in hell. Didn't faze him in the least. You know what his response was? He said, 'Somebody's gotta win, and you can't win if you don't play.' He was right."

"Did he ever win?"

"Not that I know of." Hilts smiled. "But the point is, he could have. He was in the game, not just on the sidelines. He was a player. That's what we are."

"You're a romantic, Virgil; an incurable romantic." She leaned over and kissed him on the cheek. He blinked, then blushed furiously.

"Hilts," he answered. "Just Hilts."

They finished lunch and then loaded the magnetometer array into the inflatable.

"You seem to know what you're doing," said Hilts, watching as she stowed the equipment in the stern of the little boat.

Finn shrugged off the compliment. "I've used them before on my mother's digs in Mexico and Belize, usually on land. They're really nothing more than sophisticated metal detectors."

They took the boat out to the reef line then turned and began to cruise parallel to the little island, keeping just outside the broken line of white water that marked the coral shoals where the *Acosta Star* had gone down, at least according to Tucker Noe. They made one run to calibrate the magnetometer pod dragging behind them, accounting for the presence of the Widgeon, then turned and came back along the same line. They found what they were looking for with remarkable ease. The ping in Finn's headphones was almost deafening.

"Are you sure?" asked Hilts.

"It's something pretty big. Either Tucker Noe was right and it's the *Acosta Star* or it's leftovers from the Cuban Missile Crisis."

"Not something organic?"

"Not unless the reef is made out of cast iron instead of coral," she answered, shaking her head.

Hilts took out the Garmin portable GPS locator Mills had lent him and took a reading that identified their exact location, then tossed out a lead line to get some idea of the depth they were looking at. The line slacked at slightly less than fifty feet.

"How can it be that shallow?" asked Finn. "We know they've had other divers here before—nude ones from Katy, Texas. Surely they would have spotted something this big."

"Maybe not," said Hilts. He pointed to the lead line, dragging away to the north, pulling out of his hands. "We're at the tag end of the reef and there's quite a current; we're almost in the channel. Sport divers wouldn't come this far unless they were looking for something in partic-ular."

The small waves lapping at the side of the rubber dinghy were cold. Finn looked up. The sun was dying in the west, somewhere beyond Cuba now; the further side of the afternoon. It was still light enough to dive, but not for long. It would take the better part of an hour to get suited up and prepared, and they'd already had a hectic day. She trailed her hand in the tropical water. Beneath her fingers the wreck of the giant ship waited silently, as it had for half a hundred years, secrets still locked within her wave-torn, coral-encrusted hull. She looked to the south; there was a deepening streak of silvery gray. Storm clouds were gathering over the distant horizon.

"Tomorrow?" said Finn.

"Tomorrow," Hilts answered. "If the weather holds."

32

They reached the wreck at fifty-five feet, following the anchor line from the dinghy on the surface down to where it stood hard against the current, the cast aluminum mushroom of the anchor itself tangled in the old twisted cables of a lifeboat davit amidships on the starboard side. The wreck was gigantic, a massive torpedo shape in the green-blue water, the dark hull clear against the white sand of the ocean floor. It seemed to stretch forever, the stern hard against the reef, the weed-and-shell encrusted bow jutting out slightly into the long sandy chute leading to the channel. The wreck was corkscrewed, the bow tilting downward, the amidships section and the stern still intact but rolled slightly to one side. From where the line came down from the dinghy it was easy to see why the huge hulk had remained undiscovered for so long. High above they could see the choppy surface just off the reef. The weather had turned ominous overnight, but they'd decided to chance the dive anyway.

Hilts pointed upward and his voice echoed electronically in Finn's earpiece. "She must have been rolled against the reef wall during the hurricane when she sank," he said. "Over the years the tidal surge and the current carved out that lip-and-groove formation."

Finn saw what he was pointing to; it was as though the water had scooped out a bed for the sunken ship to sag into, the overhang of coral throwing a long, broad shadow that would hide her from view. She could feel the suck and pull of the surge against the rebreather unit snugged onto her back plate. With the tide ebbing it was easy enough to counter, but she knew it would get steadily stronger as the dive wore on.

"Let's get going," she said. They'd been up since first light, planning the dive against the deck plans. They'd assumed, correctly from the looks of it, that the upper superstructure of the deckhouse, sundeck, boat deck, and promenade decks had pancaked into each other as she sank, like a building imploding, crushed by the weight of the two large funnels as they collapsed. According to the news reports there had been an explosion in the boiler room, but by the looks of the twisted plates and the hull it was the bow section that had torn away.

"Can you tell where we are?" Finn asked. She turned slowly in the warm water, looking up and down the confusing length of the immense vessel. Her weight belt kept her poised, negatively buoyant in the blue-green ocean. She moved her arms back and forth in a slow, sweeping gesture, just enough to keep her upright. At a guess she would have said they were somewhere ahead of where the bow funnel had been, partway between it and the forward mast.

"Somewhere just behind where the bridge would have been," Hilts answered.

"That means we have to head back toward the stern," she said. "According to the plans the main gangway doors and the lobby were a hundred and sixty feet from the bow."

"Fifty feet back," Hilts said with a nod. He unclipped a Sea Marshall Diver's Beacon from his vest, attached it to the anchor line and set the pulse light flashing. If either one of them got turned around or the weather turned bad quickly, the light and the 121.5-megahertz signal being transmitted from the device would lead them back to the anchor line.

They swam slowly to the edge of the collapsed deck and Finn stopped suddenly, brought up short as she found herself suddenly looking down to the ocean floor as the hull dropped away. The sense of size was almost dizzying; even under water it was almost enough to give her vertigo, regardless of the fact that she couldn't actually fall off the edge of the ship.

"Intense," said Hilts, treading water beside her.

She nodded and launched herself over the side, her legs and hips moving in a smooth undulating technique that was meant to reduce silt disturbance. She planed down the side of the hull, breathing evenly, enjoying the full face mask and the fact that she didn't have to keep a mouthpiece clamped between her jaws. The oddest sensation was the ebreather's lack of bubbles. The simple, even hissing of the unit and the boiling sensation of the bubbles' release around her was vaguely claustrophobic; it was almost too quiet. On the other hand, the silence let her glide through the local schools of bluefish and cobia almost without notice. In the distance she could see a smaller group of silvery barracuda swimming in their distinctive, nervous zigzags, but she ignored them; she knew the needle-toothed creature's reputation was built more on appearance than actual danger. On the rare occasions that the predatory fish attacked humans it was because they'd been attracted by some glittering piece of jewelry or a brightly reflective watch.

She planed down, aware of Hilts beside and just behind her. She kept her eyes to the left, watching the weed-and-barnacle-covered deck plates, the steadily strengthening surge moving the wrack back and forth like waving fingers. Regular lines of portholes ran off into the distance, most of them still intact, the thick glass covered in a crust of silt and growth, the cabin interiors on the other side of the barrier dark and unwelcoming. The ship was dead, not even a ghost; this was no *Titanic* with the specters of a thousand passengers still hovering nearby; this was a burnt-out hulk.

"There," she said finally, pulling up short and pointing ahead and down. A dark hole gaped in the side of the hull. It was close to a perfect square, the edges softened by a dense mat of sea growth. "The main entry hatch. It's wide open."

"They would have taken off the passengers through there while they still had the time. Easier to load the lifeboats from here."

Both Finn and Hilts were carrying high-intensity twin lights, one lamp fixed to their back plates, the other clipped to their belts. Both were powered by battery packs that had a charge life of almost two hours. They switched on and the entranceway was suddenly lit up brightly. They had agreed on position and protocols the night before, so there was no need to discuss it again now. Because Finn was smaller, Hilts would go first to assess their best route; if he could get through a space, then it stood to reason that Finn could follow. Finn on the other hand would be the one keeping track of the time, regularly checking the dive computer dangling from her vest. It would be easy to get so far into the wreck's interior that they would run out of time; it would be up to her to call the cutoff point no matter how close they'd come to their objective.

"Top to bottom," said Hilts. "We start with the Vatican guy."

"Augustus Principe, the bishop. Upper Promenade Deck, Gelderland Suite. Cabin number seventy-one." Finn reached down, pulled up the dangling computer on her vest, and set the elapsed time function. The computer would let out a loud buzz at the halfway point—their signal to turn back, no matter what. The digital display began to count down. "Go." She dropped the computer. Hilts eased forward, keeping his swim-fin motion to a minimum to reduce disturbance of the accumulated silt that had settled on board. He kept one hand extended, sweeping his hand light back and forth. Finn came in behind him and a little above, pacing herself to him.

Ten feet inside the entrance was a pile of debris, rotted wood, metal, and a pile of something that might have been a heap of life preservers, now reduced to a layer of black muck forming an environment for half a dozen kinds of weed and deep-sea undergrowth. In the light from Hilts's lamp Finn could see that there had once been a set of interior doors that swung on a central hinge in the middle of the entranceway.

Hilts kept moving. Finn followed him into the interior of the midships lobby. A school of small, flashing fish turned and slid quickly away from the searching light. There was a faint haze of hanging algae in the water. On the walls, covered with silt but still clearly visible for what they were, Finn saw a series of aluminum ornaments, each one depicting a different zodiac sign. She'd seen pictures of how they'd once looked in Mills's photo albums. Once upon a time the walls had been wood-paneled and the deck covered in some sort of nonstick tile, but all of that had long since been eaten away, leaving nothing behind but a dark, unwholesome vegetable skin. On the left the light picked out the open counters of the chief steward's office and the purser's office. The night before they'd discussed the possibility of checking the purser's office, but eventually had decided against checking it out. The purser would no doubt have a safe, but it was unlikely that Devereaux or even his colleague, Bishop Principe, would have kept anything valuable there. They'd check it if they had the time, but only as a last resort.

Above their heads the false ceiling had sagged, revealing a tangle of pipes and electrical conduits. Some of the panels had collapsed and others looked half melted. The heat from the fire if not the fire itself had reached this far. They pushed a little farther, passing what appeared to be Sagittarius. A door sagged. Hilts shone his light. A row of empty dentist's chairs looked into a row of blank, silt-covered mirrors.

"Barbershops?" Finn guessed.

"Or beauty salon," Hilts responded, his voice crackling in Finn's earpiece. Another few feet and they had their answer. A second room and a second row of weedy chairs. A further scattering of armchairs tangled in a heap. Mirrors cracked from side to side, silt and muck inches thick on the floor, visible here and there in patches of black and white geometric tile. A chessboard. There'd been a postcard in one of the souvenir books. This was the men's barbershop, which meant the first had been the women's beauty salon.

"Stairway next," Hilts's voice murmured in her ear. "I'm going to attach a line if I can find a tie-off."

"Hey!" Finn yelled, pulling up, a dangerous flash of livid green appearing out of the corner of her eye.

Disturbed by the movement of the divers or perhaps the light, a huge green moray eel surged up out of the ooze and silt beneath one of the barber chairs, huge teeth bared in its beaklike head. A yard long and shaped like a thick, fleshy sword blade, the bright green horror twisted between them, snapping its powerful jaws, then whipped away into the gloom at the edge of the cone of sharp illumination thrown by Hilts's light. The moray, had it struck, could have easily taken her hand off. Even a small laceration could have led to a vibrio bacterial infection that could cause gangrene within hours.

Finn let out an explosive breath, fogging her mask for a few seconds. Her pounding heart began to slow to something like normal again. She gritted her teeth and kept on swimming, turning toward the wide staircase that opened before her, caught in Hilts's light. Who knew how many sharp-toothed horrors lay along the path of their explorations.

"Tuesdays with moray," she muttered, embarrassed by her jerking reaction to the eel. "Pardon?"

"Nothing," Finn answered. "You had to read the book." She took a breath and let it out slowly. "Let's keep on going."

Hilts nodded. He unclipped the Dive Rite primary reel from his vest, attached it to the end of the aluminum stairwell banister, and clipped the no-snag device back onto his vest. It held two hundred and fifty feet of braided nylon line that would guide them back to the main lobby on their return if their visibility was obscured by too much silt.

The stairway had been tilted almost to the vertical by the sinking of the ship. Debris had rained down from above, mostly ceiling panels and small pieces of furniture. The remains of a chandelier were strewn down the steps, barely recognizable in the weeds and muck. There was even more algae here, suspended in the water, caught like gently swirling dust motes in the seeking beam of their lights.

They reached the top of the stairs without incident and eased their way down the narrow corridor to the left. Over time the ceiling tiles, loosened by the collapsed decks above, had torn free, releasing the plumbing pipes and cables running through the narrow space. They swam forward, frog kicking rather than using a flutter stroke, but even so the silt thrown up by their passage soon reduced visibility to almost nothing. Hilts kept his light on the starboard line of doorways, most of which yawned open. Ten minutes brought them to suite seventy-one.

"This is it." Hilts rubbed at the dark algae that covered the sagging door, revealing an engraved rectangular plaque screwed to the metal surface. The deeply etched lettering was still faintly visible: GELDERLAND. The photographer swung the beam of his light into the entrance. "Looks messy. Careful." He reached down to his vest, unhooked the reel and looped the nylon line around the straight handle of the door and let the reel fall. He headed into the room with Finn behind him.

A fire, a hurricane, and nearly half a century under-water had taken their toll. In the old photographs Finn had seen an image of what had passed for sophistica-tion in the early 1960s: modern-looking tufted vinyl chairs arranged around a glass-topped circular plastic table and a thin, Mondrian-patterned carpet in vivid colors, king-sized bed with a padded vinyl headboard, long, low Swedish Modern bureaus with long, low matching mirrors, wood-veneer wall covering in burled walnut that was actually printed fiberglass, and a row of four portholes, square rather than round, for no other reason than being different.

The publicity shots showed women wearing yellow cocktail dresses, drinking martinis and smoking cigarettes in holders while their men stood by with smiles on their square-jawed faces, usually holding a modern straight-stemmed pipe in one hand and a cut-glass tumbler of some amber liquid in the other.

Things had changed.

There were no men in tuxedos or women in cocktail dresses; they'd fled the burning vessel a long time ago. Coat hangers, the waterlogged ruins of an old suitcase, and some kind of curtain material hung on a row of plastic hooks in the little foyer inside the entrance. The floor was thick with muck and sediment. Farther in, the room was almost impassable and the visibility virtually nonexistent. Their lights passed over floating pieces of what might have been the old padded headboard; the office-style easy chairs around the table had disintegrated into the thick layer of dark silt on the deck where the Mondrian carpet had rested, and the fiberglass wall paneling had peeled away from the hull plating, heated red-hot in places according to the survivors. Aside from the remnant of the vinyl suitcase, there was no sign that anyone had ever occupied the cabin.

Finn pushed against the inner door frame of the foyer and glided across to the low chest of drawers. She tried to pull open one of the compartments and the entire piece of furniture silently came apart in her hands. There didn't seem to be any surface not covered with a layer of algae or slime. There was nothing in the drawer except more silt.

"There's nothing here," said Hilts, swinging the light around. "If there had been it would have disappeared a long time ago."

Finn checked her dive computer. They'd been down for more than an hour. It was time to go. "We have to get out of here," she said. "We should still see if we can get to Devereaux's cabin at least."

"Okay," said Hilts. He swung around, his fins sending up a blur of silt from the floor. The beam from his light glinted on something beneath him.

"Wait," said Finn. She reached blindly down into the haze of newly disturbed muck, hoping that there wasn't another eel lurking in the dense ooze. Her fingers touched something hard. She grabbed it, pulling upward. Hilts tilted the light onto the object.

"I'll be damned," said Hilts's voice in her ear. "A big gold crucifix."

"Better than that," said Finn. "It's a bishop's Pectoral Cross. The question is, where's the bishop?"

"Maybe he left it behind."

"If I remember correctly, they're not supposed to take them off."

"Let's try Devereaux's cabin."

"All right."

Finn stuffed the six-inch-long gold cross into her dive belt and swam after Hilts, following him out of the submerged cabin. Hilts gathered up the Dive Rite reel and they began retracing their route, moving silently back through the gloomy corridor, rewinding the line as they went in a ritual that dated back to ancient Crete and the silken thread that saved Theseus from being lost in the Labyrinth. Even though their fins had kicked up the ooze to almost zero visibility on their way in, they made their way back to the central staircase and the Main Deck foyer without any difficulty.

Hilts waited, suspended above the stairwell, moving languidly, waiting until Finn rejoined him. They dropped down the tilted stairs, keeping just away from the silt-and-algae covered walls. The farther down they got the worse the visibility became. Somewhere between the time of the fire and the present a whole section of the A Deck area below the Main Deck had collapsed, pushing tons of debris along the canted corridor like garbage down a chute. They reached the A Deck foyer and could go no farther; the stairwell was completely jammed with sections of wall paneling, tangles of pipe, and enormous amounts of unidentifiable debris, all of it made even more dangerous by the choking weed and silt. Even if it had been physically possible to tunnel through the barrier of junk, there was no telling what had taken up residence in the deadly barricade over the years.

"Now what?" said Finn. In front of them were the smashed double doors leading into the main dining salon. On the other side of the foyer it looked as though there had been some large mosaic made of colored tiles, most of which had fallen out over time. On either side of the mosaic were the brass doors of the two elevators serving the amidships section of the ship. Hilts swung the beam of the light into the dining salon. In the pictures, the original Princess Oriana Dining Room, named for the opera, was a lavish, two-story, domed monstrosity complete with an eight-piece orchestra and yellow tufted leather ceiling. There was seating for five hundred at a time, and somewhere with a series of hidden escalators for the stewards to retrieve orders from the kitchens below. Now it was a murky waterlogged cavern, the carpeted floors rotted to soggy, crab-infested destruction, the leather ceilings long decomposed, the remains hanging in long organic strings like the putrid entrails of some massive sea creature's innards. The tables, all bolted to the floors, were still there, their linen cloths long gone, the padding of the chairs no more than muck. The orchestra balcony hung like an empty eye socket over everything. No ladies in yellow dresses, no officers in dress-white uniforms solicitously lighting politically incorrect cigarettes; the tomb of a vanished era of elegance.

"This place is really starting to give me the creeps," said Hilts.

Finn lifted her computer and stared through her mask. "We're running out of time. We can check out Devereaux's cabin, but we'd better be quick about it." Both of them could feel the distinct tug of the tidal surge as it swept through the giant wreck. It was much stronger than it had been when they first approached the ship.

"How long?" asked Hilts.

"Fifteen minutes in, ten on-site, fifteen back, no more," Finn answered.

"Gotcha."

"How do we go in?"

"The elevator shaft, like we agreed."

"Can you get the doors open?"

"I can try." Hilts took the lightweight Dutch Guard titanium diver's pry bar off his belt and pushed across the lobby, skimming lightly toward the ornate brass doors, now deeply pitted with corrosion and dark with oxidization and plankton slime. Finn followed close behind.

They paused in front of the doors, Finn using her hand light this time, throwing a patch of illumination on the tarnished barrier before them. Hilts used his hand to wipe a small patch clean in the center and fitted the hook end of the bar into the crack. He pulled but the effort simply swung him around in the water, raising a cloud of silt.

"Need to get some kind of purchase," he muttered, and tried again, this time lifting one leg, slipping off the big Dacor flipper and putting his bare foot against the frame of the doorway. He heaved again and the door separated, a dark split appearing. Finn swam forward, hooking the light back on her buoyancy vest, and helped him pull the doors fully open. She unhooked her light and Hilts switched his on as well, leaning into the shaft and throwing the beams downward. The light showed an empty shaft, thick with floating plankton that seemed almost to have a breathing movement as it rode the invisible surges and currents in the water.

"Looks clear," said Hilts.

"Don't forget the reel; that stuff in there looks as thick as soup."

Hilts nodded, put his flipper back on and retied the safety line to a jutting beam on the side of the elevator shaft. He swam into the shaft proper, reached up, and then adjusted his vest compensator.

"Going down," he said, grinning through the mask. He sank slowly into the shaft as the deflated vest reduced his buoyancy. Finn waited until he was clear of the doorway, then followed him into the shaft. She hit the yellow punch button on her vest, heard the gargling, bubbling hiss of escaping air, and then began to drop even deeper into the sunken hull of the old wreck.

The A Deck elevator doors slid open with no difficulty, and Hilts and Finn swam easily out into the foyer. This was the first full accommodation deck with no shops or dining facilities. Toward the bow were two corridors, port and starboard, with inside cabins down the center. Devereaux had been down on the passenger list as occupying cabin 305 along the left corridor, which now stood directly in front of them.

They pointed their lights down the dark tunnel and saw nothing but a few weeds and a thin layer of sediment and silt over everything. There was no sign of fire or damage, which made sense since the origin of the disaster lay far astern in the after-boiler area. Trailing the safety line behind him as it spun off the reel on his belt, Hilts eased himself across the lobby and down the dark passage, careful to disturb as little of the silt on the deck as possible. A narrower side passage to the left led to cabins 319, 323, 320, and 324. The doors were all open, the cabins beyond dark and forbidding, cluttered with the ruin of their rotted interiors. Next came three singles in a row, 315, 313, and 309, with matching inside cabins on the other side of the hall. Once again the doorways to all of these were open.

"Almost there," said Hilts quietly. They swam a little farther. The door to Devereaux's cabin—305—was firmly closed.

"Strange," said Finn. "According to all the reports the crew went from cabin to cabin making sure no one was left behind."

"Which is why all the doors are still open," commented Hilts.

Finn swam forward and grasped the door handle. She pulled it down but it remained in place.

"Jammed?" said Hilts.

"Feels like it's locked," Finn responded. She tried again. Still nothing.

"Let me," said Hilts. He moved in beside her and tried for himself. "You're right."

"Use the bar," Finn suggested.

Hilts nodded. He took the titanium pry bar off his belt and jammed it into the seal of the door just at the level of the handle. He pulled hard and there was a soggy crunch. With his free hand he tried the handle. It moved downward. He pushed and the door opened, swinging inward.

"Who locks his door when the ship is on fire?" asked Finn, hovering behind him.

"Let's find out," Hilts said. "Give me a time check first."

Finn consulted her dive computer. "Ten minutes starting—" she hit the elapsed time button—"now."

Hilts put the pry bar back on his belt, switched on his hand light and moved into the cabin, pulling himself in on the doorframe. In the old brochure for the ship Finn had seen at Mills's home on Hollaback Cay, the A Deck cabins were quite a bit different than the larger room occupied by Bishop Principe. As well as the simple size difference, Devereaux's cabin was the mirror of Principe's, with the little vestibule on the left rather than the right. Beyond the coat rack and suitcase storage area was a second door that led into the cabin proper. Beyond that was a pleasant bedroom/sitting room area with a large wood-paneled wardrobe against the aft bulkhead and a dressing table and mirror against the forward wall. The bed itself was located under a pair of small, square portholes looking out onto the sea, or in the present case looking out over the abyss of the reef edge down to the distant ocean floor. Hanging from an overhead track was a nylon privacy curtain much like the ones around a hospital bed.

Directly opposite this was the entrance to the bath-room and the second bed. In between the two beds was a sitting area occupied by a pair of vinyl-covered armchairs and a small, round, plastic-topped coffee table with an image of a compass rose laminated under the surface— the logo of the Acosta Line, seen everywhere from bar coasters and menu covers to the carpeting on the floor of the dining rooms.

"Dear God," whispered Hilts, his light sweeping around the room. The room was almost exactly as it had been half a century before. The locked door had kept out most of the marine life visible in the rest of the ship, and unlike an older vessel like the *Titanic,* most of the fabrics and materials used in the *Acosta Star* were synthetic and not as prone to decay. The result of this was that the only sign of the passage of time was a fine layer of silt and sediment over everything, rather like a layer of sheeting over the furniture in an empty house. The only obvious symbols of decay were the human remains on the bed.

The cartilage and the tendons holding the bones together had long since been eaten away and the skeleton had fallen apart, but enough shape remained to show the curled-up fetal position of the body. The long bones of the leg were bent, the ribs had fallen into a yellowing pile, and the arms were brought up almost as if the man had been in prayer at the time of his passing.

"Who is it?" Finn said, floating closer to the pile of bones scattered on the sagging bed. Above her the remnants of the nylon privacy curtain waved in the currents like old shrouds.

"Devereaux, presumably," said Hilts. "Someone locked him in his cabin by the looks of it. Either that or he committed suicide. Looks like cause of death was asphyxia. He didn't burn to death or drown." The photographer moved lightly above the bed and checked the portholes. "They're dogged shut; he couldn't have opened them without a pipe wrench."

"He was a Catholic. I doubt if it was suicide," Finn said, turning her light and shining it across the room to the far wall.

"I guess we're fifty years too late to find out whatever his secret was," said Hilts.

"Maybe not," Finn said quietly, her light falling across the little round table. "What's that?"

The surface of the table had a skin of silt and sediment, but there was obviously something underneath. Finn waved her hand back and forth just above the tabletop, unsettling the thin layer and dispersing it.

"Playing cards?" said Hilts, looking confused behind his mask.

"I bet they're Kem brand," said Finn. "My father used them when he played bridge on his digs in the jungle. They're made out of cellulose acetate or something; that's why they haven't disintegrated."

The cards were tucked into the aluminum rim of the table in two groups, like poker hands, faceup. One set was at the top edge, the other set to the left. The top set had six cards, the set on the left had five. "He wasn't playing poker, that's for sure," said Hilts, looking down at the cards.

"He wasn't playing any game," replied Finn.

"A message?"

"He was locked in here, he knew he was going to die, and he took the time to do this. He had to have had a reason."

"A three, an eight, another three, a pair of twos, and a five in one hand, a pair of eights, the jack of diamonds, and another pair of twos, clubs and spades." He paused. "What kind of message is that?"

"The only one he could leave. We just can't decipher it." She checked her computer again. "And we don't have any time left. Take some pictures and let's get topside." The suck and blow of the current was beginning to take its toll in the cabin, pushing sediment up and obscuring visibility.

Hilts nodded, unzipped the big ninja pocket on his vest and took out the compact DC500 Mills had purchased for him in Nassau. He took a full set of general pictures of the cabin using the internal flash, then concentrated on the table and its two hands of cards. "There's something else there," said Hilts, pointing to the center of the table. Finn waved her hand, sweeping away more of the brown sandy grit, and a gleaming line of gold appeared.

"It's a chain," she said, picking it up. It was a little more than two feet long, the links finely made. The clasp was still intact but there were two end links torn open. "It's as though someone tore it off someone else's neck," said Finn.

"Take it and let's get going," Hilts replied. He took a shot of the dangling chain and then Finn stowed it away in her vest. Hilts stowed the camera again, then turned and made his way out of the cabin, Finn holding her light so that it shone over his shoulder as he reeled in the safety line on their way back. Even in the lower corridor the increase in the tidal surge could easily be felt, and now there was the steady booming sound transmitted down to them as heavy waves hammered into the side of the reef. By the time they reached the Main Deck foyer again the surge had become truly fierce, the current pushing them from one side to the other, slamming them against the bulkheads as the ocean breathed through the gaping entrance doors. The weather on the surface was clearly closing in. Finn thought about the rubber dinghy and the half mile of sea that lay between them and landfall at the lighthouse.

Silently the couple angled their way across the lobby, fighting against the bursting current as it tried to push them tumbling back. Finn knew that their margin of safety was slowly slipping away. Another ten minutes or so and they'd be in real trouble. She'd heard a hundred stories of divers who were within sight of the surface but doomed never to reach it because they let their dive run too long. No air was no air, and the human body could only survive for so long before the lungs sucked a fatal dose of drowning seawater. At least with the rebreathers they wouldn't have to make decompression stops after such a long period on bottled air.

"Getting bad," Hilts commented, trying to pull and glide his way to the entrance. He finally reached it. Finn came in behind and above, hanging on to the upper edge of the broad hatch in the side of the ship. Outside the sea had darkened perceptibly, the sun from above cut by at least half. The strength of the tidal surge plucked at their buoyancy vests, the harsh current moving first in one direction, then rebounding to the other. There was roughly a ten-second pause of relative calm between them. "We'll have to time it exactly right if we want to get back to the anchor line in one piece," instructed Hilts. The line was snugged around the lifeboat davit four decks up. If they missed the calm between the surge and its backwash they'd either be slammed mercilessly against the hull or swept out into the channel. Finn had always been curious about traveling to Cuba, but not enough to be a waterlogged corpse washed up on one of her white sand beaches.

"What about a safety line?" Finn suggested.

Hilts shook his head. "Too much drag. It would slow you down. Just wait for the pause and then swim like hell. If you feel the return stroke coming, find something to hang on to, quick, got it?"

"Got it."

They waited in the entranceway as the surge poured in through the opening, sweeping them back. As it faded Hilts hit the green full buoyancy button on his vest and shot out through the hole, rising quickly out of sight. Hilts counted to herself. At ten she tensed and waited. The surge came again, passed through, heading for the wall of the reef, and then the movement stilled again. Finn hit the green button on her own vest, kicked hard and rose up through the water, watching for Hilts's waiting figure by the anchor line. She decided on her way up the huge, curving side of the hull that if he wasn't there she'd simply keep on going up to the surface and pray she'd arrive within a reasonable distance from the inflatable. She tried not to think of the hundred other possibilities, none of them good.

She kept her mask up as she slipped up the barnacle-and-coral-encrusted side of the ship, keeping herself well off, trying to judge the strength of the surging current at her back, wondering if she had enough time left before it smashed her against the hull. With her vest at full rise, the shells and fire coral with its poisonous, jellyfish stingers and its spiky exoskeleton would tear her to ribbons. Suddenly the line of the open deck appeared and there was Hilts, hand out to grab her just as the surge hit, pushing them both hard. Finn managed to weather the beating of the surge using her free hand to hang on to the anchor line and then it was momentarily calm again.

"I didn't think I was going to make it," she said, her breath coming harshly.

"I was having my doubts there for a second as well," Hilts replied, the sound of his voice crackling and breaking up in her ear with a hiss. "And we're not out of it yet." He let go of the line with one hand and pointed upward. Finn stared. Fifty feet above them the water was in a torn fury, the vortices of the waves smashing in all directions, filling the water with bubbling turbidity. Finn knew the surface was quickly turning into a nightmare. The approaching storm was almost upon them; they had to reach shelter soon or they'd be in very bad trouble.

"We've got to get topside—now," she said.

"No argument from me," agreed Hilts. "Let's go."

They waited for the next surge to pass then followed the line up to the top, hanging on with one hand and guiding their progress with the other. Amazingly the inflatable had ridden out the rising weather and hadn't swamped. Finn's head broke the surface and she saw that things were worse than she'd thought. Through the beaded water on her face mask she could make out the far horizon. It was a black horror of scudding clouds that seemed to rise up like a terrible wall. They'd surfaced in the middle of a raging, moaning gale, and from the looks of the horizon the gale was only a taste of much worse to come. She tugged the mask up and over her face as Hilts reached the surface beside her. Both of them clung to the dangling side ropes of the dinghy as the cold rain lashed at them with talons of icy spray. Suddenly, impossibly, there was the sound of a bullhorn close by. They turned toward the sound and stared in disbelief.

It was Rolf Adamson, fifty yards away, standing spread-legged on the corkscrewing rear deck of a Viking 56 supercruiser yacht with the name *Romans XII* across the transom. He had the bullhorn in one hand and a pump-action shotgun dangling from the other. "Mr. Hilts, Miss Ryan! Please! You must come out of there instantly, I insist! You'll catch a chill if you're not careful!"

33

A damson was dressed in white duck trousers, a blue denim shirt, and black Topsiders without socks. He sat on the far side of the boat's large and lavishly decorated salon in one of the big tan leather club chairs scattered around, a cut crystal tumbler full of single-malt whiskey in one hand and the Lucifer medallion in the other. Beside him, in jeans and a Harvard sweatshirt, was Jean-Baptiste Laval, the supposed expert in Coptic inscriptions. Finn and Hilts, dressed in long fluffy bathrobes with *Romans XII* embroidered across the right chest, sat together on one of the long low leather couches arranged around the bulkheads. Adamson gestured at the bathrobes with the hand holding the medalion. "You understand the significance of the name, don't you?" he asked.

Finn spoke before Hilts had time to open his mouth. "Of course," she said mildly. "It's from the Bible. Romans twelve, verse nineteen. Vengeance is Mine sayeth the Lord."

Adamson was impressed. "Very good, Miss Ryan. I had no idea you came from such a religious family."

"I didn't. Just a reasonably literate one," said Finn.

"It's actually *Romans XII* the second, to be really accurate," Adamson said and smiled. "My grandfather owned the first one. A Boeing fifty-foot Bridgedeck. He used to come out to Cay Sal Bank with Joe Kennedy and Cardinal Spellman to bonefish before they went on to Havana."

"Your grandfather. This would be Schuyler Grand, the wacko radio evangelist?" asked Hilts. Finn wondered how smart it was to overtly provoke a man with a shotgun up against his chair.

"That's correct, Mr. Hilts."

"Doesn't sound like the Schuyler Grand I knew," the photographer answered.

"That's the point, Mr. Hilts, you didn't know him. Few did. He was a very complicated man."

"He was crazy," said Hilts flatly.

"He certainly was." Adamson smiled. "He was crazy as a bedbug, but there was nothing crazy about his patriotism. He believed that America was the greatest nation in the world and that it had been created to lead the rest of the planet away from godless communism and into the light of true democracy."

"That story's a little out of date," said Hilts. "All the people who sang that tune are dead and gone, from Stalin all the way down to Richard Nixon."

"The names have changed but the enemies haven't," Adamson answered. "America is faltering once again and it needs a strong patriotic leader to save it. A man of God. A man *for* God."

"Why do I get the idea that man is you?" said Hilts sourly.

"Do you know what a killer culture is, Mr. Hilts, Miss Ryan?"

"Genghis Khan, Attila the Hun. Barbarism as a culture," offered Finn.

"Osama bin Laden," said Hilts.

"Most people find the idea abhorrent. They think that a barbarian is simply someone who hasn't seen the light. But that's not the case. There are killer cultures all around us but we're too vain, or isolationist in our thinking, to believe it. There is no way that Islam and Christianity can ever coexist. We are both killer cultures. Cultures who kill their enemies as a way of life. Hitler knew that, but his vision was too shortsighted. If he'd made war only on his true enemy—Communism—he would have captured half the world and lived to a ripe old age. The Prophet said to 'make slaughter' on the Infidel and Christian dogma tells us to 'smite the anti-Christ.' There can be no middle ground. This is a crusade. One way of thinking must win in the end. And we're losing, except we refuse to recognize that fact. We no longer have the highest standard of living in the world. Workers in Canada and places like Brunei earn better wages. Korea has better longevity statistics. Cuba's population is more literate. Progress has been turned into a dirty word and our president would rather see us as asexual Puritans. We have turned ourselves into a nation of scapegoat seekers who look for their cultural pleasure in reality shows that are anything but. I intend to put a stop to that and the Lucifer Gospel will help me do it."

"You're as crazy as your grandfather," growled Hilts.

"Why do I get the idea that both of you are crazy?" Finn asked angrily. "There's a hurricane coming and the two of you are talking politics."

The broadloom deck beneath her feet was tilting back and forth in long slow swells and the sound of the wind outside seemed louder every second. It was dark enough for the overhead lights to be on in the huge, low-ceilinged room, and rain scratched harshly against the long, teardrop-shaped windows. The whole boat yawed back and forth, turning on its anchor chain, keeping its bow into the wind.

"Don't worry about the hurricane, Miss Ryan. So far the weather people have it listed as a tropical storm. They haven't even given it a name. I'm afraid you won't live through it anyway. As for myself and my companions, this boat is capable of slightly more than fifty miles an hour running ahead of the wind, and run we shall as soon as we've disposed of you."

"So where does he fit in to all of this?" Hilts asked, nodding toward Laval.

"I don't think that's any of your business," said the Frenchman.

"Brother Laval is a Jesuit," said Adamson. "Which means that above all he is a logical man. Brother Laval no longer works for the Church. He works for me."

"So, Laval, I guess that means that money talks and God walks."

"Very witty, Mr. Hilts," replied the monk. "Perhaps you should get a job as an action hero."

"How did you find us?" Finn broke in. "You couldn't have followed us."

"We didn't. We followed your friend, Mr. Simpson."

"I'd never met him before I came to Cairo," Finn protested.

"Simpson is the reason we hired you, Miss Ryan," said Adamson. "Simpson's been part of this since the beginning." He laughed. "Since before the beginning really."

"What's that supposed to mean?"

"Rumors about a Gospel written by Christ have existed almost from the time of His Crucifixion," said Adamson. "And rumors like that have always had a political currency. My grandfather was aware of that fact. In the late twenties, when the Vatican was in serious financial trouble, my grandfather, among others, came to their aid. An exchange of information regarding the Lucifer Gospel was made. It's a very long story and I have neither the time nor the inclination to tell it now, but suffice it to say that eventually governments became involved. Mussolini's, ours, and the British, who basically held the reins of power in the Middle East at that time."

"Simpson."

"Simpson." Adamson nodded. "The Lucifer Gospel, had it surfaced at that time, could have seriously altered the balance of power immediately prior to World War Two. It could have crippled the Vatican's newly acquired tax base and it could have brought America into the war at least a year, if not two years, earlier."

"Water under the bridge," commented Hilts.

"Not really. When DeVaux reappeared in 1959 with news of the Gospel, the Cold War was at its height. The revelation of the Gospel's existence and its existence within the United States would have had an enormous impact. Jack Kennedy, should you need reminding, was a Catholic."

"The Pope killed Kennedy?" Hilts laughed. "That's a new one!"

"His Catholicism may well have been a contributing factor to his death."

"You think this lost Gospel is still that important?"

"Our own government thought so, Miss Ryan. DeVaux died for it on the Acosta Star."

"Kerzner, the Canadian?" said Finn, remembering Lyman Mills's theory.

"Your father was his control officer, Miss Ryan. Kerzner was CIA. His real name was Joseph Turner. He wasn't Canadian, of course, but by then DeVaux was an American university professor and the Company's mandate didn't include assassinating our own people, as you are well aware, Mr. Hilts. Not back then, at any rate. His job was to find out what DeVaux was selling the bishop, and barring that, to kill both of them, which he did. Now it's your turn."

"We didn't find anything either," said Finn.

"That remains to be seen," said Adamson. He took a small sip from his glass. "Not that it matters to you." A pair of heavyset men in dark clothing appeared at the doorway to the big cabin.

"What are you going to do to us?" asked Finn.

"I'm not going to do anything, Miss Ryan, God is."

-

By the time they were taken out onto the rear deck of the yacht, the rain was coming down in ragged torrents and the visibility was nonexistent. The ocean around the boat had been torn to ribbons, a mass of broken, spume-flecked chop and huge rolling waves that vanished in the sodden curtain of rain to break like thunder in the hidden distance. The sky overhead was a black roiling mass of clouds driven to madness.

"The robes, please," said Adamson. They stripped them off, leaving them in their bathing suits. There was no sign of their dive vests or other equipment. The inflatable had vanished and the float plane was gone. "Follow the sound of the breakers. That's Cay Lobos," said Adamson, shouting to make himself heard over the sound of the storm. "Micah, verse three, chapter three: *'Who also eat the flesh of my people, and flay their skin from off them; and they break their bones, and chop them in pieces, as for the pot, and as flesh within the caldron.'* That's what the coral is going to do to you, and if that's not enough, the highest point on the island is twelve feet above sea level. During the last half dozen hurricanes in this area the storm surge was twice that. You two are about to have an unfortunate accident."

"Why are you doing this?" Finn asked, shivering. "You have the medallion. Without it we have no proof of anything. You have what you wanted."

"I need your silence, just as your father needed DeVaux's silence and DeVaux needed Pedrazzi's. The secret of the Lucifer Gospel can't be shared." He waved the shotgun in his hands. "Down onto the swim platform, please." Finn looked over the side. Four steps down, the wide lip of the teak-decked swim platform jutted out from the rear of the yacht. The breaking seas curled over it in long steady sweeps. Beyond that the waves were a tangled hell. Once they went overboard they wouldn't stand a chance.

"What if we refuse, then what?" asked Hilts.

"Then I'll do the Lord's work for him and blow your brains out," answered Adamson, hefting the shotgun. "The barracuda won't mind the mess and neither will the sharks. Up to you." He motioned with the pump gun again. "Over you go."

Hilts grabbed Finn by the wrist and pulled her toward him. "When we go over don't try to stick with me and don't try and help me if you see I'm in trouble. Take care of yourself, forget about anything else." He turned, gave Adamson the finger and went down onto the platform. Within seconds a roller swept him off his feet and he vanished. Finn went after him and stepped down onto the platform, taking a deep lungful of air as she did so. Instantly she was swallowed by the darkness of the sea.

The first of the huge rollers pulled her down and under in a single, ice-cold moment of absolute terror. As a child she'd once been briefly caught by an undertow in the warm waters off Cancun, but she'd instantly been snatched to safety, plucked out of the water by the strong hand of her ever-vigilant father. There was no one to save her now. The deadly surge grabbed her in its watery fist and pulled her relentlessly toward the bottom.

Finally she broke free of the wave's terrible grip and gulped in huge gasping lungfuls of air, retching seawater, feeling the tug of the next wave as she was swept forward and down, with barely enough time to take a breath before the deluge swallowed her again. Once more she was pressed down, thrown onto the reef, the rough sand and coral tearing at her skin, and once more, exhausted, she clawed her way to the surface for another retching breath.

A third wave took her, but this time instead of coral there was only sand on the sloping bottom, and she barely had to swim at all before she reached the surface. Her feet stumbled and she threw herself forward with the last of her strength, staggering as the sea sucked back from the shore of the tiny island in a rushing rip current, strong enough to bring her to her knees. She crawled, rose to her feet again and plunged on, knees buckling, in despair because she knew in some distant corner of her mind that another wave as strong as the first could still steal her life away with salvation and survival so tantalizingly near.

She staggered again in the treacherous sand that dragged at her heels and almost toppled her over. She took another step and then another, blinking in the slanting, blinding rain. Ahead, farther up the strip of shining beach, was a darker line of a few trees, fan palms and coconuts, their trunks bent away from the howling wind and the lashing rain, unripe fruit torn away, crashing away in the teeth of the storm like cannonballs. Finn's breath came in ragged gasps and her legs were like deadweights, but at least she was free of the mad, clutching surf that broke behind her now like crashing thunder.

Struggling higher up the sandy slope she finally reached a point above the wrack and turned back to the sea, sinking down exhausted to her knees. The straps of her one-piece swimsuit were torn. She was still badly fright-ened, but wept with relief as she stared into the shrieking nightmare of the rising hurricane. She was alive.

Through the rain she could see the heaving broken line of frothing white that marked the reef, but nothing more. True to his word, Adamson had run before the wind and disappeared. Suddenly she felt something touch her shoulder and she turned, screaming. She whirled, heart in her throat. It was Hilts, a gash on his forehead streaming blood, his hair plastered down, grinning like a lunatic. He had survived as well.

"Misery acquaints man with strange bedfellows!" he said, yelling happily into her ear.

"What are you talking about!?"

"Adamson's not the only one who can quote things!" Hilts yelled. "How about:

Full fathom five thy father lies;
Of his bones are coral made;
Those are pearls that were his eyes:
Nothing of him that doth fade
But doth suffer a sea–change
Into something rich and strange."

"The Bible?" asked Finn.

"Shakespeare," said Hilts. "Miss Slynn's grade-nine English class. *The Tempest*. Had to learn the whole damn play. First time it's ever come in handy." He took a deep breath and let it out slowly. "Come on," he said. "Even Caliban knew to get in out of the storm."

34

Finn woke to the terrible, windborne crying of the gulls and the savage echo of broken surf pounding on the reef. She vaguely recalled the night before in brief images and sensations: the pressure of the mounting wind, the monstrous sounds of nature unleashed, the harsh, pervasive slanting rain so powerful at times it almost stole her breath. The sound of water swirling at her feet. The knowledge that there was no hope left.

Instead of hope there had been the fickle randomness of storms. Late in the night and early the following day the wind had veered a mere two points in a new direction, the hurricane had shifted its wheeling carnage overhead and slipped away, and finally the waters had receded. In the cold lens of the NOAA cameras roughly twenty-three thousand miles overhead, the pinwheel of the hurricane cloud began to shred and tear.

Opening her eyes, it took her a moment to realize that she was lying just inside the entrance to the abandoned hut next to the lighthouse. The dead cat was gone and so was most of the litter. The cat's ghost still occupied the hut with its musky, dead animal odor. The strap on her bathing suit had been repaired with a neat reef knot. There was no sign of Hilts. Finn suddenly realized that she had a splitting headache. She was also cold.

Shivering, she sat up. She looked around. Somehow the sheet-metal roof of the hut had managed to stay nailed to the rafters, and it was obvious that Adamson's prediction about the island being covered by the storm surge had not been borne out because, thankfully, she was high and dry.

Finn stood up, still groggy, and ducked through the entrance. The sky was hammered blue, the sun a blinding disk as it rose in the east, and the sea was like liquid metal, dark lines of heavy breakers destroying themselves loudly against the line of the invisible reef.

There was a strange, unpleasant taste in the air, like hot blood on tin or what she imagined death by electrocution would smell like. She made her way down to the spot where the marram grass met the sand and dropped down, hugging her knees as she stared out to sea. She realized that she was both hungry and terribly thirsty. She heard a faint sound and turned; Hilts was approaching from down the beach, hauling what seemed to be their flotation vests behind him.

In his other hand he was dragging the limp body of a large, brownish-gray bird with a long sharp beak and legs like sticks. The front of his once white T-shirt was stained pink with his own blood, and the gash in his forehead had scabbed over in a horrible-looking mass of caked blood and serum. His lips were bruised and covered with a cracked white layer of salt. His eyes looked bloodshot and feverish but he was smiling.

"Finished your beauty nap?"

"I'm thirsty," she said, her voice croaking.

"Go back to the lighthouse. There's a few puddles around the base. Drink up now because they'll evaporate soon enough, and I couldn't find anything to store water in." He lifted the dead bird by the neck. "I'm going back to the hut. Start a fire with one of the vest flares. Cook up old Ichabod here. Found him with a broken neck up the beach a ways. We might die of thirst but at least we won't starve to death while we're doing it." He gave her a grin, then plodded up the beach, heading for the hut. Finn climbed to her feet and headed for the lighthouse at the other end of the narrow little spit of land.

By the time she drank her fill and returned to the hut Hilts had already gathered driftwood and debris and had a blazing fire going, initiated by one of the emergency flares in the dive vests. He was on his knees in the sand in front of the hut, busily gutting the large, heronlike bird with his vest knife. He held up the blood-covered, razor-sharp tool and smiled.

"Adamson must have thrown the vests in for authenticity."

"Maybe he'll come back to see if we survived," said Finn. "Did you ever think about that?"

"Why would he bother?" Hilts said. He scooped the bird's entrails into his hand, pulled hard, then threw the guts downwind along the sand. The gulls screaming above them in the air dropped out of the sky and began to tear at the offal like vultures.

"The fact that we survived last night at all is a miracle. We're not going to last for very long without water. Unless Fidel's navy finds us or we're visited by your friendly neighborhood cocaine runner, we're pretty much screwed." He found a long piece of driftwood, speared one end into the bird's stomach cavity, and laid it across the flames. The feathers began to smoke and burn. It smelled horrible.

"That's disgusting," said Finn.

"That's lunch," Hilts answered.

After the bird had spent almost an hour in the flames, Finn tried the charred sour meat, and after throwing up she returned to the steadily drying puddles that lay around the concrete pad of the lighthouse in a gleaming string of little lakes, fading like mirages as the Caribbean sun rose overhead. She dragged herself back to the fire in front of the hut. The remains of the heron carcass had been discreetly removed. Hilts now had the dive vests laid out on the sand and was picking them over.

"Six flares, two knives, a reel of safety line we could maybe use for fishing if it wasn't so big, an aluminum mirror, two personal first aid kits, two dive computers, a Garmin IPX7-Z series submersible GPS unit, and some shark repellant. They always seem to have more useful stuff on those reality TV shows." He put a hand to his mouth in mock horror, eyes widening. "Could it be that reality TV isn't real after all?"

"I'm not quite sure what you're so happy about."

"It's all relative. We could be dead but we're not."

"But we soon will be by the sound of it."

"Maybe the Buff Divers will show up from Katy, Texas, you never know." He shrugged. "Hope springs eternal in the human breast," he added philosophically.

"The man who said that also said, 'walk sober off; before a sprightlier age comes tittering on, and shoves you from the stage,'" said Finn.

"Show-off," replied Hilts. He squatted in front of his little pile of booty like one of the dealers in the City of the Dead bazaar in Cairo.

"I've never really understood how GPS works," said Finn, staring at the exotic Garmin unit that looked like an outsized bright yellow cell phone in the pile.

"It's pretty simple really," Hilts explained. "It was originally designed by the military. They shot up twenty-four satellites into stationary orbits around the earth so two of them were always above the horizon anywhere in the world. They had base-station receiving units on the ground that picked up the signals broadcast by the satellites and triangulated off them to give you an exact location. The system was put into use just in time so that our boys didn't get lost in the Iraqi desert." He picked up the unit and switched it on. "The ones they have now are a lot more sophisticated. Like little computers. With the right map chip it's like having an atlas in the palm of your hand. This one has North America and the Caribbean programmed into it." He looked down at the display. "That's us: eighteen degrees, fifty-five minutes, sixteen seconds north, sixty-six degrees, fifty-four minutes, twenty-three seconds west."

"What did you say?" Finn asked.

Hilts sighed and repeated himself. "Eighteen degrees, fifty-five minutes, sixteen seconds north, sixty-six degrees, fifty-four minutes, twenty-three seconds west."

"That's it," she said, nodding.

"What's it?"

"The cards. The way they were arranged on the table in Devereaux's cabin. The table had the Acosta Lines logo on it, a compass, remember?"

"A compass rose, right," he answered, nodding.

Finn closed her eyes, concentrating.

"A three, an eight, another three, a pair of twos, and a five to the north. Thirty-eight degrees, thirty-two minutes, twenty-five seconds north." She paused, trying to remember. "Two eights, a jack, which stands for ten, and a pair of twos on the west side of the table."

"Eighty-eight degrees, ten minutes, twenty-two seconds west," filled in Hilts, keying the figures into the unit. He stared at Finn. "You're a genius!"

Over the water, in the distance, Phil Stubbs was singing about a group of tadpoles celebrating their journey to frogdom, backed up by a chorus of squeaky six-year-old girls telling what da froggies say. Squinting into the sun, Finn saw Tucker Noe's ancient flatboat appear around the reef, heading past the lighthouse toward them. It looked a little battered by the storm but it was still afloat. Phil's singing became louder, his strong voice carrying easily across the water to them.

"Kalik," said Hilts, pronouncing it like a native and licking his lips.

"What are the coordinates for?" Finn asked, keeping her eyes on the decrepit old boat just to make sure it was real.

Hilts looked down at the Garmin unit.

"They was hoppin' and skippin' an jumpin' an leapin', come back to the pond, come see," sang Phil.

"Rutgers Bluff, Illinois."

35

Rutgers Bluff was located a dozen miles downstream on the Winter River from Fairfield, the county seat. That part of Illinois always had more to do with hillbillies and hicks than Oprah and the Miracle Mile, and if you were looking for a movie to describe it, you'd think of *Deliverance*, or maybe *In Cold Blood*. Most of the local population was of German descent and there weren't many foreigners. You might have been born there and you might have stayed there through no fault of your own, but if you were thinking of opening a convenience store, Wayne County and Rutgers Bluff wouldn't be your first choice.

The most common crimes in the county were rape, petty larceny, assault, and car theft, in that order. More people were on the county payroll as police than any other category. Names like Bruner, Ostrander, and Koch were common, and the white squirrel was the county animal, appearing on police patches and the stationery of county departments. No one could remember who Rutger had been but the bluff was still there, a stumpy, tree-covered escarpment that overlooked the river at what the locals called the Third Chute.

Long ago lumber had been an important part of the Wayne County economy and logs had been sent downstream to the big mills at Parkman. At the big rapids along the course of the Winter River wooden chutes had been built to convey the logs around the turbulent white water. Rutgers Bluff was the third set of these. The Fourth Chute was located two miles downriver at thirty-eight degrees, thirty-two minutes twenty-five seconds north, eighty-eight degrees, ten minutes, twenty-two seconds west, the numbers set out in plastic playing cards by a dead man aboard a sunken cruise ship several thousand miles away to the south a little more than half a century before.

"This can't be right," said Hilts, looking first at the handheld Garmin unit and then at the bruised, desolate scene around them. It was pouring rain and both he and Finn were soaking wet, even though they'd picked up a pair of cheap rubber ponchos and two rain hats at a sporting goods store in Fairfield. They were standing in front of their rental Ford on an old steel bridge across Winter River just above the rapids. From end to end the bridge was no more than fifty feet long and was just barely wide enough for two cars to pass. On one side of the bridge was rough brush country, second-cut old spruce and pine and miles of gray swamp and slash. Directly in front of them was an open meadow beside the river. A tumble-down barn stood on one side of the road and a farmhouse and several outbuildings on the other. A rustic summer-camp-style sign had been erected over a narrow track that led past the farmhouse to the outbuildings. In roughly trimmed pine branches the arching sign read: CAVERNS OF WONDER.

To the left of the entrance, propped up on the old split-rail fence, was a plywood cut-out of Jesus painted with a yellow halo that looked more like a straw hat and brown sandals that looked vaguely like army boots.

A blue-and-white Mary leaned against the other side of the gateway. Apparently the Mother of Christ had been a blonde. The paint looked very old and faded. Below the "of" in Caverns of Wonder another square of plywood had been added that read: "$10." White on black.

"This just can't be right," Hilts repeated. "Caverns of Wonder? This is a tourist trap. Or was. It looks deserted."

"Do the numbers match?" Finn asked.

"Exactly."

"Then this is it." She nodded toward the plywood Savior. "Jesus of Illinois. Bit too much for coincidence, don't you think?"

"It's a joke."

"Too many dead bodies to be very funny. And if it is a joke, our friend Adamson is going to be seriously ticked off."

"You think he's figured it out?"

"He had your digital camera. If he hasn't got it figured by now it won't be long."

They climbed back into the car and drove beneath the arching sign. They parked in an old gravel lot beside what might have once been a snack booth or a gift shop. Behind it was a makeshift row of outhouses. Grass had grown up everywhere. The hinges on the big front flap of the snack booth had rusted through and the flap sagged like old skin. A little to the left on a small rise of land was the farmhouse. The roof sagged and the chimney had collapsed. It was a blind and dead place. The front yard was a sea of brambles, with the wreck of an old truck by the front door, an International Harvester Scout, blue and white and rust. The tires were rotted away and the cracked windshield was covered in bird droppings. Everything was gray in the rain.

"*Twilight Zone,*" murmured Hilts, looking out across the parking lot. At the far end was the burnt-out hulk of what might have been a school bus.

"I was thinking more along the lines of *Nightmare on Elm Street.*"

"Part twenty-six: *Jason Takes Rutgers Bluff.*"

"So what do we do now?" said Finn.

"Check it out. See if this was what Devereaux really found."

"Is there anything about this place in the guidebook you bought?"

They'd picked up a local guide in the same place they'd bought the ponchos and the rest of their things. Hilts picked the small booklet up off the dashboard and leafed through it.

"Fourth Chute, Winter River. First discovered by English cabinet-maker and infamous drunkard Tom Woodward in 1829. Woodward fell down a sinkhole and had a vision of the Redemption after being trapped in the lightless caverns for six days. For the rest of his life Woodward decorated the caves in a glowing tribute to his religious conversion and sobriety. His Shrine of the Holy Mother in the Ninth Grotto has been the site of several miraculous and unexplained natural and unnatural events. Ten-dollar admission. Includes prayer pamphlet and glow-in-the-dark Caverns of Wonder key tag. Bus Tours welcome. Parking. Refreshments." Hilts closed the book. "Natural and unnatural events."

"Glowing key tag."

"This is not what Devereaux discovered."

"Yes, it is," said Finn. "At least part of it. He died leaving a clue to this place. There must have been a reason."

Hilts sighed. He reached across her and took a flashlight out of the glove compartment. "Come on."

She followed him out of the car and into the grinding rain. It was the kind of rain Noah must have faced; not much in itself, but relentless, as in Northern Ireland, where it hasn't stopped raining for a thousand years, merely paused from time to time. They crunched across the parking lot to the screen of trees and the burnt-out bus. On closer inspection, she thought the bus had probably been the source of the Refreshments mentioned in the guide. The remains of a scorched metal sign offered hot dogs, Stalactite Burgers, Stalagmite Chili, and fresh-cut Bat Fries. A path to one side led between the trees and down a rocky path that led toward the river.

"Listen," said Finn, putting a hand out and grabbing Hilts's arm.

They paused.

"I don't hear anything," he said. "The rapids. The rain."

"Keep listening." Deep behind everything else was a steady chattering sound, muffled and distant. Every few seconds there was a stuttering thump.

"What is it?" said Hilts, finally hearing it. "A generator?"

"A pump," said Finn, after a long moment. "A sump pump, like the ones they use on flooded basements."

"Down in the Wonder Caves?"

"Caverns of Wonder," corrected Finn.

"Whatever." The photographer sighed.

"Maybe something automatic that starts up when it rains."

"I'd like to see that warranty," scoffed Hilts. "Nobody's had this place as a going concern for years. Decades maybe."

They were headed downward, the trail actually becoming a set of steps cut into the stone. Hilts saw a crushed and flattened soda tin on the ground and picked it up. Recognizably Coca-Cola. Even in its condition it was obvious that it had been opened with an old-fashioned spear can opener. "How long ago were zip tops invented anyway?" He threw the can into the bushes.

"In 1962," said Finn. "A guy named Ermal Fraze from Dayton. My mother went to grade school with him. I wrote a paper about it for an archaeology class: 'Interpretation of the Zip Top opener as ornament or tool; aids for the historian of the future.' I got an A."

"You should have been committed. Ermal Fraze?"

"Ermal Fraze," she said and nodded. "Strickley Elementary School. Mom says they have a plaque. Girl Guides Honor." The steps flattened into a broad plateau overlooking the rapids and the quieter water beyond. Half shrouded by young sugar maple saplings, wet green in the rain, was the entrance to the Caverns of Wonder. The bare limestone above it showed undulating cakey layers filled with dirt and moss, slick and muddy. The entrance itself had been squared off with timbers so old they seemed part of the stone around them. There were the remains of a heavy plank door, but it had long ago been torn off its hinges. There was a sign over the entrance like the one on the gate, only smaller, branches nailed to plywood, the upright for the *D* in Wonder missing so it read CAVERNS OF WONCER. Rainwater was running down the squared log steps leading down to the hole. There was a handrail made of a gray, dead and rotted spruce bough.

"Looks wet," said Hilts

"That's because it's raining," replied Finn. "It'll be drier inside."

"Famous last words."

"Are you coming or not?"

"Lead on."

Finn went down the steps carefully, holding on to the rail. Hilts was close behind. As she passed beneath the entrance he snapped on the flashlight. There were more steps beyond and a maze of supports and roof beams. The steps went down into darkness. It looked more like an abandoned mine shaft than a holy grotto. So far she hadn't seen anything even faintly religious. Her mind flailed around desperately trying to find some connection between an old limestone solution cave on the banks of a raging river in southern Illinois and a gold medallion in the possession of a mummified corpse in the Libyan Desert.

Based on the actions of Adamson and his colleagues the connection was more than tenuous—in fact, it was as solid as a steel bar. Solid enough for them to kill for, and more than once.

The steps ended and became a meandering boardwalk through a series of roomlike openings that were barely worthy of the word "cave," let alone "cavern." It looked as though at some point the Winter River or some tributary of it had cut through the rocks and over time had worn a narrow pathway, rarely wider than an arm span. Here and there along the walkway were stalactites and stalagmites and lavalike tables of accreted stone, but for Finn, who had been raised in a world of Mayan tombs and subterranean archaeological sites, the Rutgers Bluff Caverns of Wonder were pretty small potatoes. A minor show cave or roadside attraction, like the giant concrete egg she'd once seen in Men-tone, Indiana, or seven-story concrete statues of Jesus in Arkansas. What was here that could have affected the outcome of World War Two or interested anyone in the Vatican? It was absurd.

"There," said Hilts.

"What?" she answered, stopping as his voice brought her away from her thoughts. He switched off the flash-light. Suddenly the narrow, arched cave they were standing in was alive with green, glowing images.

"Glow-in-the-dark key tags," said Hilts. A goggle-eyed Jesus looked down from a stalactite. Mary prayed by a pool of stone. Fish swam across the ceiling with teeth like sharks' and tails like guppies'. The Sermon on the Mount was rendered in knobs and blobs of stone painted with staring faces, and banners were crudely lettered with quotations from Scripture.

"Like the Haunted Mansion at Disney World," said Finn. "Only God is doing the haunting."

"It's awful," said Hilts, staring. They continued along the boardwalk and into the next cave. It was the size of a front porch and about as exciting. It was also grotesque. A huge Last Supper undulated across the arching ceiling, like a huge picnic table in flight, Apostles and cherubs and clouds, Judas with a hairline like Dracula and a winding tale like a bad dream by William Blake. Tasteless, talentless, and badly researched. Christ facing left instead of right,

Simon the Zealot with long hair rather than bald, chalice in front of Christ when there was none. Thirteen disciples, not twelve.

Now that's interesting, thought Finn. Even an illiterate who was even remotely Christian in this nation knew there were twelve, although almost no one except a priest or minister could actually name them. She had specialized in religious art of the Renaissance and she wasn't sure she could do it herself. She stared up at the gigantic, hideous meal floating above her on the stony dripping ceiling and ticked them off in her mind, left to right: Bartholomew, James the Lesser and Andrew, Judas, Peter and John, or Mary Magdalene if you were a Dan Brown fan, followed by Thomas, James the Greater and Phillip, then Matthew, Jude, and lastly, Simon the Zealot. So who was the thirteenth figure, looming off to one side behind Simon in this ghastly rendition of the world's most famous painting and second most famous literary meal? She stared. There wasn't a lot of detail in the eight-foot-tall figure glowing on a slime-covered rocky wall made even slicker by the volumes of rain seeping through from above. It was a male, wearing a robe, bearded, one arm at its side, the other raised and pointing at… what?

"The last figure on the right?"

"The one pointing?"

"That's the one."

"What about him?"

"What's he pointing at, exactly? Can you tell?"

"Looks like some kind of drapery over in the corner," answered Hilts, pointing the flashlight. On the far side of the room a large flow of soluble lime had dropped down to form a pool. When the water in the cave had receded or been pumped out there was nothing left behind except a flowing cascade of stone called a Baldacchino canopy.

"I want to take a look," said Finn. She slipped under the guardrail of the boardwalk and stepped carefully onto the wet surface of the cave floor beyond. Water trilled coldly up to her ankles. Slipping now was not an option.

"Why?"

She still wasn't quite sure, but she suddenly knew that something from her distant childhood was calling her. The excitement of opening the secret door in the wardrobe to Narnia, of entering Merlin's Crystal Cave, stepping into Dr. Who's phone booth or Ray Bradbury's Green Town, which if she recalled was also in Illinois.

"Did you know that they call this whole part of Illinois Little Egypt, and nobody knows why?" she called out, her voice echoing in the semidarkness. She kept carefully in the cone of light thrown by Hilts's flashlight and concentrated on the slippery footing.

"I didn't know that, no," said Hilts, following her off the wooden boardwalk.

"Some people say it's because southern Illinois supplied a lot of grain to the north in the bad winter of 1830-31. Other people say it's because the confluence of the Mississippi and the Missouri reminds them of the Nile Delta. For some reason people gave places a lot of Egyptian names around here: Cairo, Karnak, Dongola, and Thebes. Even Memphis, if you want to stretch a point. They even have a giant glass pyramid for a basketball arena."

"I'm not sure I see the point."

"If you're in a Catholic church, where do you hide a candle?"

"With all the other candles," he answered.

"Exactly," she said. She reached the Baldacchino canopy, braced herself, and slid around to one side.

"What?" Hilts said, coming carefully up behind her.

"I think I found it," she whispered.

"What?"

"The candle." She moved two feet to the right and disappeared before his eyes. Hilts stared, playing the light over the waterfall-like slab of ancient flowstone. There was no sign of her.

"Where are you?"

"Right in front of you," said her disembodied voice. Suddenly she was there again, her bright face and wet, spiky dyed hair shining in the flashlight beam.

"How did you do that?"

"It's the Caverns of Wonder. A miracle."

"Show me."

"Give me the light and take my hand."

He put his hand in hers and squeezed. She squeezed back and he handed her the flashlight. Suddenly the cave was plunged into total, blind man's darkness, the complete absence of light. She tugged his hand and he slipped behind the canopy with her.

Hilts found himself in a stiflingly small passage directly behind the oozing apron of rock. It was a space so close he could feel the wet stone brushing against him front and back. He was in some terrible crawl space: a crack in the world.

"Oh, jeez."

"It's okay." A click echoed in the stifling space. Light flushed to the right and he saw that the narrow passage led to his right. There wasn't even room enough to turn around.

"You're kidding."

"Come on."

She shuffled to the right down the stick-thin passage, and he had no choice but to follow. It was either that or be left in the darkness. The farther he went the higher his heart moved into his throat. He thought of a hundred situations: a fall of rock, more rain, mud, simply getting stuck, glued in place. Some basic Freudian-Jungian-Stephen Kingian thing: man's unholy heart-pounding nightmarish fear of being buried alive; the slight tension as a train goes into a tunnel under a mountain of suffocating rock.

He shuffled forward, concentrating on the feel of the soft pads of flesh on her palm and the curl of her fingers around his own. She was as small and light as a child, but there was a fierceness in her that he would have associated with a drill sergeant. It was as though times like this brought out the strength in her, a steel core able to withstand the worst that man or nature had to offer. Survival instinct. Something in her DNA that went back a million years.

"Look," she whispered. Hilts suddenly realized that he'd been shuffling along with his eyes squeezed tightly shut. He opened them. Directly ahead the tunnel seemed to widen. Finn reached up with her free hand and touched the stone.

"This has been worked," she said.

"Worked?"

"It's not natural. It's man-made." She shifted along another few feet and Hilts felt as though he'd been released from jail. There was room to move. The passage had at least a foot of leeway on either side.

Hilts saw that she was right. In the pale glow from the flashlight the marks on the stone were obvious. Someone had carved out the passage in this godforsaken hole in the ground. They moved along with ease now and both of them became aware that the tunnel was gradually both turning and sloping downward. Sometimes the natural untouched stone could be seen; whoever had done this had followed the course of a natural fault. Thinking about the drapery of rock back in the cave far behind them, it occurred to Hilts that this might have once been the natural course of a stream or spring. Finn agreed.

They went on for an hour. Hilts began to have fond sense memories of the huge Heartland Big Slamble, or whatever it had been at the Interstate Denny's that morning. A cup of the worst roadside coffee in the world would have truly been a miracle at this point. The rain and the steady forty-degree chill of the caves was striking to his bones. The claustrophobia had receded but by no means had disappeared. An hour in meant an hour out if they went back the way they'd come, and his imagination was fully capable of constructing desperate, gloomy horror stories. So far at least, thank heavens, there had been no bats or other subterranean wildlife. Hilts was not a big fan of things that made your skin crawl; deserts, not storm drains, were his area of expertise. And then, instantly, the narrow path came to an end. Light.

"My God!" whispered Finn, stepping out of the passageway.

"Jesus!" said Hilts.

They were both right.

The dome rose above them in a single sweeping arc of stone, at least a hundred feet high from where they stood and half again as high from the floor of the gigantic cavern. Light shone brightly and mysteriously from a thousand niches on ten thousand figures, all of them carved by Egypt's finest stonemasons over a lifetime in the wilderness more than a millennia in the past. Bigger than the Sistine Chapel, higher than St. Peter's, it was something no one man could have even imagined in a single lifetime, let alone constructed. Every angel, patriarch, and saint was there, every mystery and splendor from the Advent to the Resurrection, from the Garden to the Ark. All swirling upward in an astounding vortex of living art ascending to the heavens. It was beyond breathtaking. Past awe. A gift of utter beauty without the slightest touch of vengefulness or retribution, divine or otherwise. Around the base of the giant room small caves were hollowed out, some still with heavy wooden doors, others blank and open, the entrances like empty eyes. Cells. Once, a long, long time ago, this place had been occupied. Now it was only a massive tomb, built for the ages, unseen.

Finn and Hilts stood frozen, stunned by the un-imagined scale and proportions of what they were seeing, diminished by a monument that could have swallowed New York's Statue of Liberty a hundred times and might even have made Mt. Rushmore look inadequate.

"What is this place?" Finn whispered. She found a set of stone steps carved before her and slowly made her way toward the bottom of the immense cavern, head back, craning her neck as she went. If the Great Pyramid at Giza had been hollow, this is what it might have looked like. A world within a world.

"Many years ago, in Thomas Woodward's time, they called this place Jeremiah's Grotto," said a voice, echoing in the enormous chamber. An old man stepped out of the shadows on the far side of the dome and approached them. "Which of course is one of the names associated with the Tomb of Christ. It is not that place, but it is interesting that such a reputation should still be associated with it." He tapped his way across the floor, weaving his way through stacks and piles and racks of narrow-necked circular jars like the clay containers of the Dead Sea Scrolls at Qumran. "Woodward stumbled on this place but he was a drunkard and a famous sinner, so no one believed him. The Keepers then simply bought his silence and cooperation with more drink."

Finn peered into the flickering half-light as the old man came forward. He was tall and only a little stooped, leaning lightly on a heavy cane. In his free hand he was carrying what appeared to be a leather bundle rolled up and tied with a bright gold chain. His hair was steel gray and cut short, almost military. He was wearing old corduroy trousers and a dark blue knitted sweater that might have belonged to a seaman. He wore old, high-button boots and steel-rimmed spectacles. His voice was flat and Midwestern, but deep beneath there was a hint of something else. A sophistication that said something of foreign lands seen long ago. With a terrible lurch in her heart Finn realized that this old man reminded her of her father.

"Who are you?"

"The last of the Keepers."

"Keepers?"

"Keepers of this place. Its stewards, if you will." He smiled sadly. "More or less the janitor who cares for the True Word of Christ."

"I don't get it," said Hilts. "This place, in the middle of nowhere. It doesn't seem possible."

"What is the Libyan Desert if not the middle of nowhere? In relation to Rome, during the heights of empire, Jerusalem was just as much the middle of nowhere; the very ends of the earth to be exact. For Moses the Sinai was the middle of nowhere. To a New Yorker this part of Illinois is *still* the middle of nowhere. Einstein was right, Mr. Hilts; it's all relative. I could spin you exotic tales of Lost Templar Fleets, of the ocean-spanning navy of King Solomon, whose temple is mimicked in the exact measurements of the Sistine Chapel, about Nostradamus, about the New Jerusalem your friend the madman Adamson hopes to found."

"He's no friend of ours," said Finn.

"At least we beat him here," grunted Hilts.

"As a matter of fact, you didn't," said the old man. "He arrived yesterday. He's been in Olney, a few miles away, gathering equipment and information. I expect he'll be along shortly."

"How do you know that?"

"I know a great deal, Mr. Hilts. About you and my old friend Arthur Simpson, poor soul. About you and your father, Ms. Ryan." He smiled again. "It comes with the job, you might say."

Again Finn caught the faint edge of an accent in the distant past. With a breathtaking flash she had it. "You're the monk. DeVaux."

He nodded, smiling wearily.

"Pierre DeVaux, Peter Devereaux, Paul Devers now. Never a monk, though, that was a pretence. A priest always. A priest forever."

"A murderer," said Hilts. "You killed Pedrazzi. And if that's not you on the *Acosta Star,* then who was it locked in your cabin?"

"Death and secrets are hardly strange bedfellows, Mr. Hilts. Pedrazzi tried to kill me in that terrible place in the desert. He'd discovered who I was and knew I'd never let him give the secret to a man like Mussolini to use as a trading piece in some political game. He tried to kill me; I merely defended myself."

"And on the ship?" Finn said.

"In the cabin? Kerzner, the man sent to kill me by your father's people, Ms. Ryan. The man bought and paid for by Adamson's grandfather. The bishop never made an appearance. One can only presume he died in the fire."

"How did he know the exact location of this place?" asked Hilts.

"Because I told him," said the old man. "Just before I left him to die. It was his last wish."

"You really are a bastard," said Hilts, curling his lip.

"That too," said the old man with a shrug. "Most of us were. Foundlings, orphans. The refuse of life. It seemed like a good seeding ground."

"Us?" asked Finn.

"The Keepers."

"Of this place?"

"Of what it contains."

"Which is?"

"The True Word."

"The Lucifer Gospel."

"Hardly Lucifer's. He only guarded it. He was the first Keeper of the Word. This is his place." He spread his arms, staring upward into the infinity of the soaring stone above him.

"I'm getting confused," said Finn.

"I'm getting a headache," said Hilts. "I'm standing in a place that shouldn't exist lit by lights that shouldn't be burning, talking to a man who should be dead. None of this makes any sense at all."

"A thousand years ago the lights were made with mirrors, the rock was carved with the sweat and honest effort of faithful men, and the only reason I have stayed alive is to protect the secret of this place until it can no longer be protected."

"And then?" Finn said softly. "What then?"

"And then I shall destroy it," the old man said simply.

"You're crazy," said Hilts.

"Perhaps," said the old man. "But the time for the words of men like Christ is over now. There are new gods, I'm afraid." He held up the little leather-wrapped package. "When that time comes the Place of Secrets must be destroyed and the Gospel of the Light destroyed along with it. The instructions are quite clear," he added sadly.

"But why?" Finn urged. "Why destroy all of this?"

"Because if all cannot have it, no one person shall. Light is meant to illuminate, after all, it should not be used as power."

"Then tell everyone."

"The simple revelation of its existence would be used against it. It would be used as a rallying cry by Adamson and his people. This place, His Word, was not meant for that. Crusades are fought with blood and swords, not faith and sacrifice."

The shot rang out like an alien thing in the chamber, striking the old man before it was heard, whirling him around where he stood and dropping him to the floor of the giant cave. There was a series of small explosions, sharp and hard against their ears, and then, almost as though it was a signal, the light in the huge domed cavern was extinguished and total darkness fell. It remained that way for a moment and then the blackness was pierced by half a dozen brilliant narrow beams of green.

"Night-vision glasses," whispered Hilts. He felt around on the floor and found the groaning huddled shape of the old man.

"You're hit?" Finn asked.

"The shoulder. I'll live," said Devereaux. "For the moment, at any rate. Long enough."

"We have to get you out of here," said Hilts.

"You've got to get yourself out of here, before it's too late."

"We've got to get you to a hospital."

"You are two hundred and thirty-seven feet under-ground. On the far side of this cavern is an exit that leads directly to the Winter River, separated by a shield of brittle rock that I can remove at any time I wish. Adamson thinks he has won. He thinks he has triumphed. He thinks he has finally gained the ultimate prize that will give him a nation. He has found nothing. Only the darkness."

"Grab him by the legs," Hilts instructed. All around them now the green lines of light were twisting back and forth.

"Sinkholes," gasped the old man as they dragged him across the floor of the cavern. "He's coming in from the old entrances above."

Suddenly Adamson's voice boomed into the air from a bullhorn.

"I don't know how you did it, but you won't survive this time!"

"He's nuts."

"Tell me something I don't know," said Finn.

They finally managed to reach the edge of the cavern. Their backs were to the sloping stone wall. She felt the old man gripping the lapels of her jacket.

"You must get away."

"How are we supposed to do that?" asked Hilts.

"The Medusa Gate."

"What the hell is that?"

"Over each of the monks' cells a mask was carved into the stone. Medusa was the patron goddess of Lucifer's Legion. Find it and you find the way."

There was a harsh sound like tearing cloth and a flare burst overhead, throwing the dome into stark outline. At least a dozen men were rappelling down on dangling ropes from the ceiling of the cavern. All of them were armed.

"There!" Adamson bellowed. There was a burst of gunfire. Bullets ricocheted off the rock walls beside them.

The garish, hot light from the flare began to fade. Finn spotted something.

"The Medusa!" She pointed.

"Come on, bring him!" said Hilts, taking the old man under the arms again. In the last light from the flare Finn could see the wound. It was bubbling, lower on his torso than the shoulder. A lung, or worse.

"Leave me," said Devereaux weakly. "If you try to bring me you will fail. Go!" he commanded.

"We'll get help!" said Hilts.

"Go! Now!" said the old man.

They ran. The flare died out completely, leaving them in utter darkness except for the piercing lines of green. They stumbled over the rocky uneven floor of the cavern.

"One of those guys lights us up, we're toast," said Hilts.

There was another tearing sound and the air around them exploded in sudden light. There, only a few feet away now, was the small cell-like entrance marked with the same Medusa image as the one on the medallion.

"Run!" Hilts yelled, pushing Finn ahead of him toward the dark entrance. She looked back over her shoulder and saw the old man, sagging against the wall of the gigantic, wondrous place that had been in his charge for so many years. He was smiling.

Bullets flew, whining like a swarm of angry hornets. She rushed into darkness, ducking her head below the hideous, snake-haired goddess, and stumbled into the little cave. In the light from the new flare she saw that it was no cell at all but the foot of a stone stairway leading upward.

"Climb!" Hilts yelled.

She moved swiftly to the steps and began to struggle upward, the photographer close behind her, his breath harsh and grating as they pressed onward.

Minutes passed and still they climbed. Horribly, from somewhere far below, they heard other footsteps ringing on the stone. Then, with a terrible sound like the very heart of the earth breaking below them, there was a terrible roar and air pushed around them like wind from a tunnel.

"What was that!?"

"Keep going."

They kept climbing but the sound grew louder, a guttering, windy roar, and then it was upon them, a flushing horror of rock and debris that gathered them in its choking belly and pushed them upward in a tumbling torrent, hammering them with bruising force against the stone walls of the stairwell. The icy flood was like a battering ram that finally expelled them in a geyser of water on a cold stone floor. Gasping, choking, they climbed to their knees as more water flooded up from below, filling the chamber they were in.

"Where are we!?" Finn gasped, climbing to her feet, hanging on to Hilts as she rose.

"Some kind of basement," he coughed, looking around. He pointed across the swirling pool of filthy water climbing up the walls. "Stairs." He grabbed her hand and they waded across to the short stairway and climbed upward. There was a plain wooden door at the top. Hilts pushed it open and they stepped out into a musty-smelling country kitchen. There was a woodstove in one corner, an old dry sink, and a rough wood table with a few old chairs in the center of the room. Through a grimy window Finn could see out into the rainy parking lot of the Caverns of Wonder. They were in the kitchen of the old, decrepit farmhouse.

"This is how the old man got in and out, I guess," said Hilts, dropping down into one of the chairs. "Thank God it's over."

"I wouldn't get too comfortable," said Finn suddenly. There was a dangerous creaking sound all around them, then a lurching sensation as the floor at their feet skewed and twisted, as though they were in the middle of an earthquake. Hilts got to his feet again. Above them the ceiling began to crack, plaster cascading down. The floor lurched again and the window shattered as the frame twisted out of its slot.

They ran for the door leading out onto the sagging porch, barely making it before the roof behind them tumbled inward with a roar as the ruined old house collapsed inward onto itself. They raced outside into the rain and saw that the ground was cracking beneath them, huge rents in the earth appearing as the air thundered with the sound of the cavern destroying itself.

"The whole river is going to change course," Finn whispered. "We've got to get out of here!"

They ran for the car where it waited at the edge of the parking lot, reaching it just as the ground opened up and swallowed the old school bus before their eyes. Hilts got behind the wheel, fumbled at the ignition and then at last got the car started. He pushed it into drive, slammed his foot down on the gas, and they rocketed away. They reached the arching gate a second or so before it collapsed, then lurched out onto the country road and away. As the Caverns of Wonder raced behind them Finn let her head fall back against the seat, exhausted. Then, suddenly, she sat forward, frowning.

"What's wrong?" said Hilts.

She reached into her jacket and pulled out the leather bundle Devereaux had been carrying. She unwrapped the chain and saw it held a medallion like the one they'd found on Pedrazzi's body. She peeled apart a little of the leather and saw what was underneath. A scroll on metal, the copper ancient, green and oxidized, but the writing in clear cuneiform script. "The last of the Lucifer Gospel."

"He must have slipped it into my jacket when he grabbed me," she whispered hoarsely. "I didn't know."

"So now what do we do?" said Hilts, driving them away.

Finn let her head drop back wearily again and closed her eyes. Who knew what the scroll contained? What promise, what words, what power?

"I've got an idea." She smiled.

Epilogue

Finn stood on the Promenade Deck of the *Freedom of the Seas* and leaned over the side, watching as the smooth green waters of the Caribbean parted for the massive bulk of the 158,000-ton vessel. To Finn the enormous thing barely counted as a ship except for the fact that it had a relatively sharp end and a reasonably rounded one.

She knew she was old-fashioned, but to her ships were supposed to evoke some sense of passage and adventure, not simply be huge, top-heavy excuses for rock walls to climb, surf-slide wave machines, and monolithic shopping malls that floated. The boat even had its own television station broadcasting regular, enlightening programs on exactly what percentage you should tip various staff members on board.

Finn, who could remember traveling across the Atlantic on the stately and sophisticated *QE2* with her parents, wasn't particularly impressed by a ship with the naval architecture of a Wheaties box and the marketing style of a Wal-Mart. If a ship like this ever hit an iceberg it wouldn't sink, it would come apart like pieces of LEGO.

Still, it was the only way to accomplish what she wanted to achieve and it had given them an excuse to visit with Lloyd Tereo and Tucker Noe and Lyman Mills at Hollaback Cay before setting out from Nassau as the

Freedom made her inaugural cruise of the islands after her recent launch. They were well over the Tongue of the Ocean now. Finn wondered how many people jacking up their credit cards on board had even the slightest awareness of the depth of water underneath the thin metal skin of the big white ship. Barely six feet of Finnish aluminum and sheet steel between them and a two-mile drop into oblivion.

She stared out over the expanse of bright water and thought about the weed-and-coral-shrouded ghost of the *Acosta Star,* lying out there, not too far away now, hidden by the rolling ocean, keeping her secrets and her dead. Would *Freedom of the Seas* have an ending like that, a burial at sea? Not likely. In a few years, when her silly innovations became passé and were no longer cost-effective, she'd probably wind up being hacked to pieces for scrap on the breakers beach at Alang on the Indian coast, the great and terrible grave-yard for ships past their time.

For a moment, feeling the soft Caribbean breeze on her cheek, she found herself thinking about Devereaux and her father and poor old Arthur Simpson, found murdered in a ditch in Over the Hill, a dangerous and unsavory part of Nassau where an old white man had no business being. His throat had been slit and his wallet and watch were stolen, but Finn knew he'd almost certainly been a victim of Adamson's thugs.

Nothing had been heard about Adamson's own disappearance and demise beyond a press release that said the billionaire businessman had been lost during a sandstorm at the Libyan dig. There had been no mention of the Lucifer Gospel or Finn and Hilts's involvement with its discovery. According to her friend Michael Valentine in

New York, their involvement with the death of Vergadora in Italy had been put down to a case of mistaken identity and forgotten. Hilts of course was positive that Mickey Hearts's Italian connections had something to do with the whitewash.

"Hey," said Hilts, joining her at the rail. "You about ready?"

"Just about," she said and nodded, smiling.

"You're sure you want to do this?" asked her friend, a look of concern on his handsome face. His eyes were hidden behind the amber lenses of his sunglasses, but he was frowning. "We're talking about an incredibly valuable historic artifact."

"Devereaux was right," she said quietly. "For the Gospel or any part of it to fall into anybody's hands would be the wrong hands." Behind her a twelve-year-old in a bikini was trying to climb onto a surfboard on the machine-made roller in the pool behind her. It sounded like a washing machine coming alive. "Some secrets should remain secrets, some mysteries should remain mysterious."

"Then why did he give it to you?" asked Hilts.

"To give me the choice. To give me the chance to do the right thing." She shrugged. "Maybe to let someone else make the final decision."

"That makes you the Last Keeper," said Hilts.

Finn took the scroll, bound in leather with its gold chain around it, out of her bag. She held it in her hand tightly for a moment and then with a single, rushing movement she pitched the bundle as far as she could out into the air. Together they watched as it arced through the bright morning air, then finally hit the surface of the emerald sea and vanished beneath the waves.

"Not anymore," she said at last. "Not anymore."

Acknowledgments

Many thanks to Kara Welsh and to Claire Zion and of course to my editor nonpareil, Brent Howard. Long may you prosper.

The Finn Ryan Conspiracy Thrillers

Michelangelo's Notebook
The Lucifer Gospel
Rembrandt's Ghost
The Aztec Heresy